BEN CASEY

Annual

Contents

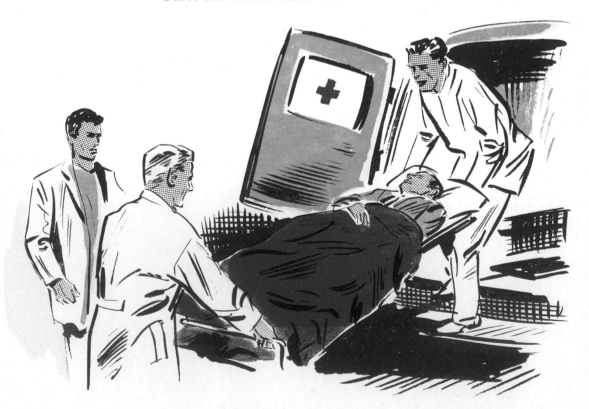

WHEN THE CAREER OF YOUNG DR. JACK SCOTT WAS JEOPARDIZED BY THE THREAT OF A SCANDALOUS LAWSUIT, BEN CASEY DECIDED TO PLUNGE INTO THE CASE TO PROTECT THE INTERNE. HIS DECISION TOOK HIM TO A MYSTERIOUS PRIVATE HOSPITAL, WHERE BEN FOUND HIS OWN LIFE IMPERILED BY THREE DESPERATE MEN READY TO.....

BEN CASEY ..

BITE THE HAND...

IT IS SPRING, WHEN CERTAIN YOUNG MEN'S THOUGHTS TURN TO THE SUCCESSFUL COMPLETION OF THEIR ONE-YEAR INTERNESHIPS. AT "59 WEST"....

DR. CASEY... CAN I SEE YOU FOR A MOMENT?

WHA...? OH, DR. SCOTT. I'M QUITE BUSY NOW WITH... WELL, COME IN.

IF I'M INTERFERING WITH ANYTHING IMPORTANT, DR. CASEY...

YOU ALREADY **HAVE**, DR. SCOTT. IT'S MERELY A MEDICAL MATTER... THE VERY LAST THING I WOULD EXPECT A YOUNG INTERNE TO FRET ABOUT.

PERHAPS LATER WOULD BE BETTER...

YOUR BLOOD TURNED TO WATER, JOCKO? THE FAMOUS DR. CASEY MAY BE THE TERROR OF "59 WEST," BUT HIS **BARK** ISN'T FATAL, IS IT?

MY NAME'S SAM SCOTT, DOC. I'M JOCKO'S BIG BROTHER.

JOCKO? OH...IS **THAT** WHAT YOUR FAMILY CALLS THE BRILLIANT YOUNG DR. SCOTT? I...UH...I'M GLAD TO MEET YOU.

DON'T TRY YOUR BEDSIDE CHARM ON **ME**, DOC. WASTE OF TIME. I'M NO PROSPECTIVE PATIENT... HAVEN'T BEEN SICK IN TWENTY YEARS. BESIDES, WE SCOTTS ARE ABOUT TO BE BLESSED WITH OUR OWN PRIVATE FAMILY DOCTOR.

I PRESUME YOU MEAN YOUR BROTHER, WHEN HE COMPLETES HIS INTERNESHIP?

THAT'S THE PRESCRIPTION, DOC. SINCE HE FINISHES UP HERE AT "59 WEST" IN ABOUT A WEEK, I THOUGHT JOCKO DESERVED A LITTLE REWARD FOR BEING SUCH A GOOD BOY ALL YEAR. I'D LIKE TO GIVE IT TO HIM **NOW**... WITH YOUR PERMISSION, OF COURSE.

I'M AFRAID I DON'T SEE WHAT **MY** PERMISSION HAS TO DO WITH A GIFT FOR...

IT'S THE KIND OF DOODAD JOCKO'LL NEED A LITTLE TIME OFF TO TEST, DOC... BEFORE I PLUNK DOWN HARD CASH TO BUY IT. YOU GOT A MINUTE? C'MERE...I'LL SHOW YOU.

A REAL CREAM-PUFF, ISN'T SHE? GUARANTEED TO CRUISE AT 125... CORNERS LIKE A DREAM... ACCELERATES TO 60 IN LESS THAN...

FASCINATING! BUT WHAT'S THIS GOT TO DO WITH **ME**, MR. SCOTT?

WHAT MY BROTHER'S **TRYING** TO SAY, DR. CASEY, IS THAT I'D LIKE THE AFTERNOON OFF TO GO FOR A TRIAL RUN IN THE NEW CAR. DR. MARINO'S OFFERED TO COVER FOR ME. I THOUGHT WE'D DRIVE OUT OF TOWN THIRTY MILES AND SORT OF MAKE AN AFTERNOON OF IT.

HAVE A CIGAR, DOC. LIGHT UP... AND LOOSEN UP.

YOUR BEDSIDE MANNER IS CERTAINLY STRAIGHTFORWARD, MR. SCOTT. NO, THANKS—I'M ON-DUTY.

IS THIS THE REASON YOU INTERRUPTED ME, DR. SCOTT?

I...I'M SORRY, DR. CASEY. PLEASE ACCEPT MY APOLO....

SAVE THE WORDS, DR. SCOTT. BE BACK HERE BY 6 P.M—WE HAVE AN INTERESTING SURGICAL PROCEDURE I WANT YOU TO SEE. PERMISSION GRANTED.

ENJOY YOURSELF, DR. SCOTT. I HOPE YOU AND SA...ER...YOUR BROTHER HAVE A PLEASANT DRIVE.

HUH? OH... THANKS, DR. CASEY. I...I MIGHT AS WELL CONFESS RIGHT NOW—SAM ISN'T THE ONE WHO'S GOING WITH ME. I-IT'S ONE OF THE... STUDENT NURSES.

STUDENT NURSES, EH? PROVES YOUR INSTINCTS ARE PERFECTLY NORMAL, DR. SCOTT. I HOPE YOU AND MISS KIRK HAVE A DELIGHTFUL AFTERNOON.

T-THANKS, DR. CASEY. WE BOTH THANK YOU... ANNE AND I.

THAT MAKES **THREE** OF US WHO ARE GRATEFUL, DR. CASEY. YOUR HEART IS SURE IN THE RIGHT PLACE.

I TRUST SO, MR. SCOTT... BUT YOUR DIAGNOSIS IS MIGHTY REASSURING FROM A MEDICAL STANDPOINT.

DR. SCOTT! BEFORE YOU BUZZ OFF... AREN'T YOU FORGETTING SOMETHING?

10

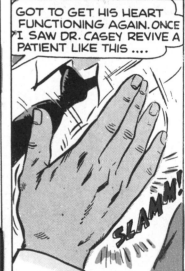

THE STREET BECOMES STRANGELY SILENT AS...

ONLY CHANCE TO REVIVE HIM... NEEDLE DIRECTLY INTO THE HEART!

I'D FEEL BETTER IF WE HAD OXYGEN HERE TO ADMINISTER. BUT **THIS** WILL HAVE TO DO. C'MON, MISTER... PLEASE... **BREATHE!**

THE DEATHLY SILENCE GROWS OMINOUS, AS THE TENSION-FILLED MOMENTS TICK BY. THEN...

OOOOH...!

HE... HE'S COMING AROUND!

LET ME GO TO MY HUSBAND. PLEASE... **PLEASE**...

HOLD HER BACK. GIVE THE DOCTOR A CHANCE TO EXAMINE THIS POOR MAN!

CARL— I'M RIGHT HERE. YOU'LL BE ALL RIGHT...

WISH **I** COULD BE AS SURE, LADY. VERY PUZZLING... CLEAR-CUT EVIDENCE OF SYMPATHETIC NERVE PARALYSIS. AND HIS EYES...

IS HE GONNA PULL THROUGH, DOC? HE STEPPED RIGHT OUT IN FRONT OF MY CAR...

HE'S NOT OUT OF DANGER YET... AND THERE'S NOT MUCH WE CAN DO **HERE**. SOMEONE BETTER CALL AN AMBULANCE... GET HIM TO "59 WEST RIGHT AWAY!

I'LL GO... I'LL CALL THE AMBULANCE.

NOT SO FAST, CHUM. YOU'RE NOT THINKING OF POWDERING ON US, ARE YOU?

GET OUTTA MY WAY, SON. I'M IN A HURRY TO... **HEY!**

I'M CLINT TAGGART... THAT'S MY OLD MAN YOU JUST RAMMED INTO. SUPPOSE WE SIMMER DOWN, WHILE I TRY TO UNTANGLE THIS MESS, HUH?

WE'VE GOT TO GET THIS MAN TO "59 WEST" RIGHT AWAY. IF YOU WANT TO HELP YOUR FATHER...

EVERYTHING THAT CAN BE DONE IS BEING TAKEN CARE OF, MEDIC. I MADE A COUPLE OF PHONE CALLS WHEN I HEARD ABOUT THIS.

ONE OF THOSE CALLS WAS TO DAD'S LAWYER... HE TOLD ME TO GET SOME ANSWERS TO A FEW QUESTIONS... LIKE WHAT KIND OF TREATMENT YOU GAVE HIM HERE AT THE SCENE OF THE ACCIDENT...

THIS IS PREPOSTEROUS! WHILE WE STAND HERE QUIBBLING, YOUR FATHER IS IN NEED OF IMMEDIATE ATTENTION AT A HOSPITAL. A COMPLETE EXAMINATION IS NECESSARY TO TELL THE EXTENT OF....

CUT THAT MEDICAL DOUBLE-TALK, DOC. IS MY OLD MAN IN CRITICAL SHAPE?

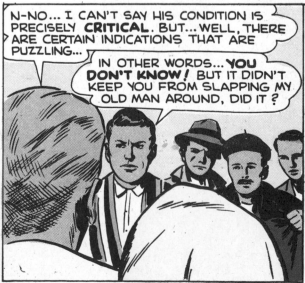

N-NO... I CAN'T SAY HIS CONDITION IS PRECISELY **CRITICAL**. BUT... WELL, THERE ARE CERTAIN INDICATIONS THAT ARE PUZZLING...

IN OTHER WORDS... **YOU DON'T KNOW!** BUT IT DIDN'T KEEP YOU FROM SLAPPING MY OLD MAN AROUND, DID IT?

YOU... YOU'RE INSANE! HIS RESPIRATION HAD STOPPED WHEN I REACHED HIM. IT WAS URGENT...

I SAW IT ALL, FELLER. IT WAS MY CAR YOUR FATHER RAN INTO. THE DOCTOR DID ALL HE COULD...

HE DID, HUH? IF I WAS THE DRIVER OF A CAR THAT CLOBBERED A MAN, I'D KEEP MIGHTY QUIET. WHEN I WANT YOUR ADVICE I'LL SEND UP A SIGNAL FLARE.

UNGHHH!

ALL RIGHT, FOLKS... LET ME THROUGH! C'MON... OUT OF THE WAY, PLEASE.

AH, THE LONG ARM OF THE LAW ARRIVES... THE MAN IN BLUE HAS TO CATCH UP ON HIS BOOKKEEPING. NAMES, ADDRESSES... THE WORKS.

A FEW MINUTES LATER, AFTER THE POLICEMAN FINISHES HIS QUESTIONING...

IT'S AN AMBULANCE! AT LEAST THEY CAN GET TAGGART TO A HOSPITAL, INSTEAD OF SQUABBLING OVER HIM HERE IN THE STREET.

RROWWRR

BUT... BUT... THEY'RE NOT FROM "59 WEST"...

NOTHING IN THE BOOK SAYS DAD HAS TO GO **THERE**, MEDIC. HIS OWN DOCTOR HAS A PRIVATE HOSPITAL... THAT'S WHERE HE'S HEADED.

YOU CAN CLIMB BACK IN YOUR SCOOTER NOW, MEDIC... THE SHOW'S OVER!

RRROWWRR

THAT MAN... I WISH DR. CASEY HAD A CHANCE TO EXAMINE HIM. HIS SYMPTOMS WERE... WELL... MIGHTY QUEER.

REMEMBER **ME**, DR. SCOTT?

R- R- RRROWRRR

HUH? OH, ANNE... I WAS JUST THINKING....

YOU SAVED HIS LIFE, DARLING — THE REST IS UP TO HIS OWN DOCTOR. COME ON... LET'S TRY TO ENJOY THE REST OF THE AFTERNOON.

THE NEXT DAY, DURING MORNING ROUNDS ...

DR. CASEY... DR. SCOTT! A FLASH FROM DR. ZORBA! HE'D LIKE TO SEE YOU BOTH IN HIS OFFICE. ON THE DOUBLE, HE SAID.

WAS IT NECESSARY TO CALL US AWAY FROM MORNING ROUNDS, DR. ZORBA? THE PATIENT IN 307 IS BEING PREPPED FOR SURGERY...

COME RIGHT IN. NUMBER 307 WILL WAIT... THESE GENTLEMEN WILL NOT.

HIYA, DOC... REMEMBER ME? CLINT TAGGART... AND THIS IS MY FRIEND, MR. LOOMIS.

HOW IS YOUR FATHER, MR. TAGGART? HAS HIS CONDITION IMPROVED, OR ... OR... ?

THAT'S PRECISELY WHY WE'RE HERE. MY NAME IS HERBERT LOOMIS, ATTORNEY-AT-LAW. I'VE BEEN RETAINED TO LOOK AFTER MR. TAGGART'S INTERESTS. FIRST ON THE AGENDA IS A BRIEF DISCUSSION OF THE ACCIDENT WHICH I BELIEVE YOU WITNESSED YESTERDAY.

NOW THAT THE HURRICANE HAS PASSED, WILL SOMEONE BE GOOD ENOUGH TO TELL ME WHAT THIS IS ALL ABOUT?

THIS WITCH DOCTOR WOULD LIKE TO KNOW, TOO. WHAT HAPPENED YESTERDAY, DR. SCOTT?

FOR THE NEXT FIFTEEN MINUTES, DR. SCOTT AND NURSE KIRK DESCRIBE IN DETAIL THE UNEXPECTED EVENTS OF THE PREVIOUS DAY....

BUT CLINT IGNORED MY ADVICE TO BRING HIS FATHER HERE TO "59 WEST FOR EXAMINATION...

SYMPTOMS ARE INTRIGUING... SOUNDS LIKE...

SOUNDS LIKE YOU'RE BECOMING ABSORBED BY A PATIENT WHO ISN'T HERE, BEN CASEY... AND A DIAGNOSIS YOU CAN'T POSSIBLY VERIFY. SAY— ISN'T SOME SICK SOUL WAITING BREATHLESSLY IN 317?

CHECK! COME ON, DR. SCOTT.

EARLY THE NEXT AFTERNOON....

SEWING LESSON COMPLETED. WHEEL THE PATIENT INTO RECOVERY, PLEASE.

I THINK SOME-ONE'S CALLING US. IT LOOKS LIKE DR. ZORBA.

YESTERDAY'S "HURRICANE" TURNS OUT. TO HAVE BEEN MERELY THE WARNING BEFORE THE STORM. MR. LOOMIS HAS STOPPED BY TO...

AT MY CLIENT'S URGING, DR. SCOTT, WE'RE ABOUT TO INSTITUTE LEGAL ACTION AGAINST YOU.

THE CHARGE IS MEDICAL MALPRACTICE! WE ARE PREPARED TO PROVE, DR. SCOTT, THAT YOUR DIAGNOSIS AND TREATMENT OF THE PATIENT—IN FULL VIEW OF DOZENS OF WITNESSES—HAS CONTRIBUTED MATERIALLY TO THE FACT THAT MR. TAGGART IS NOW ALMOST TOTALLY PARALYZED!

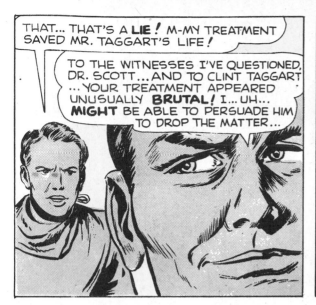

THAT... THAT'S A **LIE!** M-MY TREATMENT SAVED MR. TAGGART'S LIFE!

TO THE WITNESSES I'VE QUESTIONED, DR. SCOTT... AND TO CLINT TAGGART ...YOUR TREATMENT APPEARED UNUSUALLY **BRUTAL!** I...UH... **MIGHT** BE ABLE TO PERSUADE HIM TO DROP THE MATTER...

...IF YOU AND MISS KIRK ARE PREPARED TO...AH... **RECONSIDER** WHAT YOU SAID ABOUT THE ACCIDENT BEING MR. TAGGART'S FAULT! IN THAT EVENT, OUR LEGAL ACTION WOULD BE AGAINST THE DRIVER OF THE CAR WHICH STRUCK MY CLIENT!

YOU...YOU FILTHY SHYSTER! WANT ME TO COMMIT **PERJURY**, DO YOU?

FROM THE LOOK IN YOUR EYES, DR. SCOTT... I'D SAY WHAT YOU HAVE IN MIND IS **MURDER!** GET HOLD OF YOURSELF.

IN THIS SITUATION, MR. LOOMIS, I STRONGLY ADVISE A SWIFT RETREAT... TO MY OFFICE. CERTAIN QUESTIONS COME TO MIND...**HURRY!**

THAT YOUNG IDIOT IS IN FOR REAL TROUBLE. YOU KNOW HOW JURIES REACT TO MAL-PRACTICE AGAINST DOCTORS.

NOT AS WELL AS **YOU** DO, BUT THAT ISN'T WHAT I WANTED TO SPEAK TO YOU ABOUT.

I'VE COME TO KNOW DR. SCOTT RATHER WELL...YOU'LL NEVER GET HIM TO CHANGE HIS TESTIMONY. AS A SERVICE TO YOUR CLIENT, I WONDER IF IT MIGHT BE POSSIBLE FOR ME TO EXAMINE MR. TAGGART? WHERE IS HE HOSPITALIZED?

NOT ON YOUR LIFE, ZORBA. THE NEXT TIME ANY OF YOU PLUMBERS SEE MY CLIENT WILL BE WHEN HE'S WHEELED INTO COURT! IF HE'S STILL ALIVE AT THAT TIME...

CAN I HELP YOU, DR. ZORBA?

SEND OUT AN S.O.S. IMMEDIATELY! TELL BEN CASEY, DR. SCOTT AND NURSE KIRK TO RENDEZVOUS IN MY OFFICE IN FIVE MINUTES. QUICK...

THIS TAGGART AFFAIR PROVES CONCLUSIVELY THAT LEFT ALONE, YOUTH WILL BE SERVED... WITH A SUMMONS TO APPEAR IN COURT TO ANSWER CHARGES OF MEDICAL MALPRACTICE.

B-BUT I DID NOTHING TO BE ASHAMED OF, DR. ZORBA. ANNE CAN TELL YOU...

I HAVE THE FLOOR, DR. SCOTT. I SUGGEST YOU LISTEN TO ME CLOSELY... A CIVIL SUIT CHARGING MALPRACTICE IS BASED ON BAD MEDICAL PRACTICE DUE TO IGNORANCE, CARE-LESSNESS OR CRIMINAL INTENT.

WHETHER OR NOT THE CHARGE IS JUSTIFIED IN THIS CASE—AND I FIRMLY BELIEVE IT IS **NOT**—IT IS A SERIOUS THREAT TO YOUR CAREER...

IT WILL DELAY YOUR TERMINATION OF INTERNSHIP, MY YOUNG FRIEND. THIS, IN TURN, THREATENS YOUR LICENSING TO PRACTICE MEDICINE. WITHOUT A LICENSE YOU CANNOT START THE RESIDENCY YOU'VE ALREADY ACCEPTED. I REPEAT—THIS CHARGE IS A SERIOUS THREAT TO YOUR CAREER.

ONE, LOOMIS CLAIMS HIS CLIENT IS SUFFERING MOTOR PARALYSIS DUE TO LACERATION OF THE PERIPHERAL NERVES. TWO, HE STATES THAT DR. SCOTT FAILED TO INFORM THE VICTIM'S NEXT-OF-KIN OF THE EXTENT OF THE INJURY. THREE, HE DECLARES TREATMENT AT SCENE OF ACCIDENT WAS CHARACTERIZED BY BRUTALITY AND INTENT TO INJURE.

HE'S EITHER MAD... OR OUT FOR REVENGE BECAUSE I WOULDN'T PROMISE TO LIE IN COURT. THE PATIENT'S HEART HAD STOPPED WHEN ANNE AND I REACHED HIM, SO I RESORTED TO AN EMERGENCY MEASURE TO START RESPIRATION. LUCKILY, IT WORKED! NEXT, I EXAMINED THE MAN AND DISCOVERED DEFINITE SIGNS OF SENSORY IMPAIRMENT...

THERE WAS A STRANGE LOOK TO HIS EYES AND, WHEN HE MANAGED TO SPEAK, A NOTICEABLE THICKENING OF SPEECH. I ADVISED BRINGING HIM HERE TO "59 WEST" ...MY SUGGESTION WAS IGNORED.

EVERYTHING JACK SAYS IS TRUE, DR. ZORBA! HE SAVED THAT POOR MAN'S LIFE... AND THAT MISERABLE SON, CLINT, SHOWS HIS THANKS BY BITING THE HAND THAT HELPED HIS FATHER!

THIS WILL TEACH ME NEVER TO OFFER HELP AGAIN WHEN IT'S NOT ASKED FOR. WHAT A BOOB I'VE BEEN.

MAY I SAY SOMETHING?

PLEASE DO, BEN CASEY. I WONDERED HOW LONG WE'D HAVE TO STRUGGLE ALONG WITHOUT BENEFIT OF YOUR WISDOM.

HAVING NEITHER YOUR SENIORITY NOR POSITION, DR. ZORBA- I HESITATED TO SPEAK...

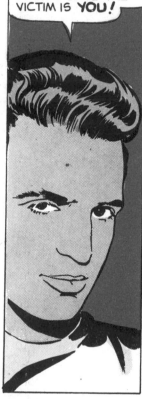

IT SEEMS CRYSTAL-CLEAR, DR. SCOTT, THAT WE'VE RUN INTO A RUTHLESS AMBULANCE-CHASER IN CITIZEN LOOMIS. UNLESS I'M WAY OFF-BASE, HE'D LEAP AT A CHANCE TO BRING ACTION AGAINST ANY DOCTOR, REGARDLESS OF THE CONSEQUENCES. IN THIS CASE THE VICTIM IS **YOU**!

ITEM ONE, JACK. IT'S TIME YOU LEARNED A BASIC FACT OF MEDICAL LIFE — UNFAIR AS IT MAY SEEM, JURIES FREQUENTLY SYMPATHIZE WITH THE PLAINTIFF IN LITIGATION AGAINST A DOCTOR.

ITEM TWO. YOU BANGED THE NAIL ON THE HEAD, MISS KIRK, WHEN YOU SAID MR. TAGGART'S SON WAS BITING THE HAND THAT HELPED... IN THESE CASES, A DOCTOR'S UNSOLICITED OFFER OF EMERGENCY AID SOMETIMES BACK-FIRES.

ITEM THREE. THE DOCTOR WHO LET'S THIS EXPERIENCE PERMANENTLY EMBITTER HIM... AND REFUSES HELP TO SOMEONE WHO DESPERATELY NEEDS IT... ISN'T AS DEVOTED TO MEDICINE AS I THINK **YOU** ARE, DR. SCOTT!

END OF MESSAGE. OVER AND OUT.

WELL SPOKEN, DR. BEN CASEY. SOMETHING TELLS ME, THOUGH, THAT YOU HAVEN'T QUITE FINISHED. IS IT POSSIBLE THAT YOU HAVE SOME CLEVER IDEA ABOUT HOW WE CAN UNTANGLE THIS NASTY WEB?

YOU FLATTER ME, DR. ZORBA... TO START, I THINK WE'D HAVE TO EXAMINE MR. TAGGART ...IS THERE ANY WAY IN WHICH WE CAN DISCOVER **WHERE** LOOMIS HAS HIDDEN HIM?

M-MAYBE **I** CAN HELP....

SNAAPP

THE AMBULANCE THAT TOOK MR. TAGGART AWAY... IT'S LICENSE NUMBER WAS **AMB-139!** IN ALL THE EXCITEMENT IT SLIPPED MY MIND. DO...DO YOU THINK IT CAN HELP?

GOOD GIRL. REMEMBERING **THAT** LICENSE MIGHT VERY WELL HELP JACK GET **HIS!**

PUT THROUGH AN IMMEDIATE CALL TO THE POLICE COMMISSIONER! THIS IS AN EMERGENCY ...A CAREER IS AT STAKE.

A FEW MINUTES LATER...

THE AMBULANCE IN QUESTION DELIVERED A PATIENT ANSWERING MR. TAGGART'S DESCRIPTION TO A PRIVATE HOSPITAL ON THE OUTSKIRTS OF THE CITY. THE INSTITUTION IS RUN BY A CERTAIN **DR. ELMER BRACK.** THIS IS THE ADDRESS!

CONFIDENTIALLY, DR. BRACK HAS BEEN INVOLVED IN SEVERAL ACCIDENT CASES OF A SOMEWHAT...AH... **QUESTIONABLE** NATURE. AS A RESULT, HIS PLACE IS APT TO BE WELL GUARDED. GAINING ENTRANCE WITHOUT A SEARCH WARRANT MAY BE A TRIFLE DIFFICULT.

WHAT WE NEED AS A GO-BETWEEN IS SOMEONE ANXIOUS TO REFER AN ACCIDENT CASE TO DR. BRACK...SOMEONE WHO LOOKS AND ACTS AS IF HE MIGHT BE INTERESTED IN A SHADY LAWSUIT...

BUZZZZ

SOMEONE HERE TO SEE YOU, DR. ZORBA! HIS NAME IS SAM SCOTT, AND HE INSISTS...

EUREKA! GADZOOKS! **SEND HIM IN!**

THAT'S CARL TAGGART, ALL RIGHT. GOT TO HURRY... THIS EXAM MIGHT TAKE SOME TIME.

JACK SCOTT'S SUSPICIONS APPEAR JUSTIFIED. SENSORY REACTION...NEGATIVE. NO RESPONSE TO HEAT...OR **THIS**...

THAT SAME MOMENT, MOVING RAPIDLY ALONG THE CORRIDOR...

CLINT... PLEASE! I SWEAR YOUR FATHER IS GETTING EXCELLENT CARE. DR. BRACK'S TREATED...

WONDER WHAT HAPPENED TO ALL THE LIGHTS IN HALLWAY?

GIVE ME ONE MORE DAY AND WE'RE READY TO PUT THE SQUEEZE ON THIS INTERNE AT "59 WEST"...

I WANT THAT, ALL RIGHT...BUT IT'S EVEN MORE IMPORTANT THAT DAD GETS THE BEST POSSIBLE MEDICAL ATTENTION. YOU'VE BEEN TREATING HIM FOR YEARS, BRACK...AND LATELY HE SEEMS TO BE GETTING **WORSE**.

IT... IT'S THE **ACCIDENT**, CLINT. CAUSED A..A..RELAPSE.

INSIDE ROOM "9"...

AHHH! THIS CLINCHES IT! I'D BE WILLING TO GAMBLE THAT TAGGART IS SUFFERING FROM CERVICAL SYMPATHETIC NERVE PARALYSIS!

MR. B-BENZORBCOTT! WH-WHAT ARE YOU...

IT'S THAT CRUMMY DOCTOR, BEN CASEY FROM "59 WEST"...

THE ACCIDENT THE OTHER DAY HAS NOTHING WHATEVER TO DO WITH YOUR FATHER'S PRESENT CONDITION. DR. ZORBA... WOULD YOU CARE TO ELABORATE?

SYRINGOMYELIA, MY YOUNG FRIEND, IS A LONG-TERM AFFAIR. IN SIMPLE TERMS, IT'S A CAVITY IN THE SPINAL CORD. IN YOUR FATHER'S CASE, I WOULD GUESS, HIS CONDITION'S BEEN DETERIORATING FOR YEARS. ULTIMATELY, WHEN ALL SENSORY REACTION HAS DISAPPEARED THROUGH DEGENERATION, THE PATIENT BECOMES INCAPABLE OF MOVEMENT, FEELING AND SPEECH!

C-CAN'T ANY-THING BE DONE TO HELP?

I REGRET TO SAY THAT THE OUTLOOK IN THESE CASES IS ALMOST UNIFORMLY POOR. IF DEEP X-RAY TREATMENT HAD BEEN STARTED SEVERAL YEARS AGO...

SEVERAL YEARS AGO...? I OUGHTA STRANGLE YOU, BRACK! YOU'VE BEEN STRINGING US ALONG, PROMISING HE'D RECOVER...

EASE UP, LAD. YOU ADMIT TO ALL OF US, DO YOU, THAT YOUR OLD MAN WAS SERIOUSLY ILL BEFORE THE ACCIDENT?

I...I GUESS IT'S NO SECRET NOW... SAY WHO ARE YOU, ANYWAY? WHERE DO YOU GET OFF NOSING AROUND....

NAME'S SAM SCOTT... I'M THE OLDER BROTHER OF THE INTERNE WHO SAVED YOUR FATHER'S LIFE. I OWN A OWN A PRIVATE DETECTIVE AGENCY. "59 WEST" HAS RETAINED ME TO .....

"59 WEST" HAS... WHAT...?

HIRED MR. SCOTT TO HELP US! SURPRISED TO LEARN, BEN CASEY, THAT AN OLD DUFFER LIKE ME IS A STEP AHEAD OF YOU? HEH! HEH! SAM'S BEEN WORKING FOR US SINCE HE LEFT YOU HERE THIS AFTERNOON.

WE'RE ALL FULL OF LITTLE SECRETS, AREN'T WE? WELL... WE'VE WASTED ENOUGH TIME. TED... JACK... GET MR. TAGGART TO "59 WEST" RIGHT AWAY.

I-I SUPPOSE YOU ALL HATE ME. BUT... PLEASE DON'T TAKE IT OUT ON DAD. ISN'T THERE SOMETHING YOU CAN DO TO HELP HIM?

MOST WE CAN DO IS USE DEEP X-RAY, AND HOPE IT ARRESTS FURTHER DEGENERATION. I SHOULD WARN YOU— TREATMENT AT THIS LATE DATE IS RARELY EFFECTIVE! OF COURSE, OCCASIONALLY...

PLEASE DR. CASEY, DO **ANYTHING** YOU CAN.

WHAT HAPPENS TO THOSE TWO VULTURES... BRACK AND LOOMIS? IF THERE'S BEEN ANY MALPRACTICE, **THEY'RE** THE GUILTY ONES.

SAM SCOTT WILL BE HAPPY TO TAKE CARE OF THEM UNTIL THE POLICE GET HERE TO TAKE OVER YOU CAN PRESS CHARGES LATER.

LATER AFTER EXTENSIVE TESTS...

TREATMENT ISN'T CURATIVE... BEST WE CAN HOPE TO DO IS STOP FURTHER INROADS OF THE DISEASE... AND WE CAN'T EVEN PROMISE THAT!

YOU'VE PERMISSION FROM ME AND MY MOTHER... DO WHATEVER YOU THINK BEST!

TELL NURSE WILLS TO START PREPPING MR. TAGGART FOR SURGERY. I'D LIKE DR. SCOTT TO ASSIST ME. ALERT DR. MAGGIE... A LAMINECTOMY IS COMING UP...

INTERCOM

THE OPERATION PROCEEDS...

ALL SET, DOCTOR.

THEN LET'S GET TO WORK. KNIFE, PLEASE.

IN CASE YOU'RE WONDERING, JACK, THE REASON FOR THIS LAMINECTOMY AND DRAINAGE IS THE HOPE THAT IT WILL AID THE LATER APPLICATION OF X-RAY. WE STILL HAVE TO CUT OUT THE SYRINX, DRAIN AND DECOMPRESS THE CORD... THEN PRAY FOR A MIRACLE!

ANOTHER HANDSOME JOB OF HEM-STITCHING, BEN!

THANKS, MAGGIE. IT'S TOO EARLY TO TELL IF IT'S GOING TO HELP. KEEP YOUR FINGERS CROSSED.

SOON AFTER THE OPERATION, DEEP X-RAY TREATMENT IS STARTED...

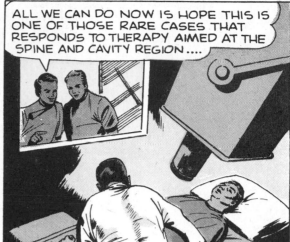

ALL WE CAN DO NOW IS HOPE THIS IS ONE OF THOSE RARE CASES THAT RESPONDS TO THERAPY AIMED AT THE SPINE AND CAVITY REGION....

SEVERAL DAYS OF INTENSIVE X-RAY TREATMENT. THEN...

YOU'RE A MEDICAL RARITY, MR. TAGGART. PROGRESS IS SPLENDID. CONGRATULATIONS.

DR. ZORBA JUST TOLD ME THE GOOD NEWS. HOW AM I EVER GONNA BE ABLE TO APOLOGIZE FOR THE CRUMMY WAY I ACTED, DR. CASEY... OR THANK YOU ENOUGH FOR ALL YOUR HELP?

BEST WAY WOULD BE TO DIRECT YOUR APOLOGIES AND THANKS WHERE THEY BELONG... TO THE INTERNE WHO MADE A CORRECT ON-THE-SPOT DIAGNOSIS, AFTER SAVING YOUR FATHER'S LIFE AT THE SCENE OF THE ACCIDENT.

YOU'RE RIGHT AS USUAL, DR. CASEY.

A FEW DAYS LATER THE YEAR'S INTERNE-SHIPS ARE COMPLETED. IN DR. ZORBA'S OFFICE, WHERE AN IMPROMPTU CELE-BRATION HAS JUST TAKEN PLACE...

THAT SPORTY BEAUTY OUTSIDE IS ALL YOURS NOW, **DOCTOR!** FROM THE LOOK ON HER FACE, I'D SAY THE ONE STANDING BESIDE YOU IS, TOO. WHY DON'T YOU KIDS ASK PERMISSION FOR AN AFTER-NOON OFF AND...

OOFFF! IF... IF I SURVIVE YOUR SEND-OFF, SAM.

SAY! THAT LOOKS LIKE DR. SCOTT AND HIS GIRL FRIEND DOWN THERE IN THE STREET. HE...HE SEEMS TO BE HAVING SOME TROUBLE...

WHY DON'T YOU GO DOWN AND HELP THEM, CLINT?

HEY! LOOK AT THAT! COME ON, DOC... LET'S GET DOWN THERE! MIGHT BE TROUBLE! THAT CLINT TAGGART IS TRAVELLING UNDER A FULL-HEAD OF STEAM!

YOU THINK IT MIGHT BE THE CARBURETOR, CLINT? OR MAYBE THE PLUGS?

YOU STICK TO YOUR SPECIALTY, DOC... I'LL WORRY ABOUT MINE! I HAVEN'T STUDIED AUTO MECHANICS ALL THESE YEARS FOR NOTHING. AHHH. NOW SHE'S PERKING.

OKAY, FOLKS... DIAGNOSIS AND TREATMENT COMPLETED. YOU CAN CUT OUT NOW. HAVE A GOOD TIME ON THAT LONG-DELAYED PICNIC.

THANKS... DOCTOR!

WHAT HAPPENS IF THEY GO A BLOCK OR TWO AND THE CAR CONKS OUT, CLINT? SINCE THEY DIDN'T ASK FOR HELP, THEY COULD SUE YOU FOR MALPRACTICE!

HUH? SUE ME FOR...? OH, DOC CASEY, I GET THE MESSAGE... I'LL NEVER FORGET IT!

TIME FOR ME TO SHOVE OFF, AMIGO. I WANNA THANK YOU FOR THE HELPING HAND YOU GAVE JACK DURING THIS BRACK-LOOMIS-TAGGART CAPER. PUT 'ER THERE!

N-NO THANKS, SAM. I NEED THESE FINGERS FOR SURGERY TODAY...

I WONDER WHO'S WORSE—THE VILLAIN WHO BITES THE HELPING HAND, OR THE FRIEND WHO TRIES TO CRUSH IT?

Gone Fishing

NOT for the first time in their famous association Dr. David Zorba was finding it necessary to speak to Dr. Ben Casey on the same, well-tried and much-discussed subject.

"Ben," said Dr. Zorba, "if I've said it once I've said it a score of times. . . ."

"More like a hundred," grunted Ben.

"Now don't try to get flip with me, young fellow," rejoined Zorba. "The truth is that somehow or other I've just got to get it into that head of yours that you need some rest. You also need. . . ."

"I know, I know," sighed Ben Casey. "I need an interesting hobby, some after-hours recreation—only I don't have any after-hours and. . . ."

"Then it's past time you did," said Dr. Zorba sharply. "I know you're dedicated to this hospital, Ben, but if you keep right on driving yourself the way you do then you'll go stale . . . besides, you simply must realize that the world is larger than this hospital. . . ."

"Sure, I know all that," replied Ben, "and maybe some of these days I'll take a little time out to observe it, but right now the demands and interests of 59 West take up all my leisure."

"They don't have to, Ben—not to the extent that you have no private life at all. It's good for a doctor to relax, and it's no less good for him to have an interest. Otherwise. . . ."

"Otherwise the tension is like to kill me, eh?" completed Ben.

Dr. Zorba could not repress a smile. "Well, now, not quite so lethal as that, Ben. But, seriously, you do need some relaxation . . . and right now is the time to take it!"

Ben spread both arms.

"Right now I got to prep a patient for surgery . . ." he began.

"I've assigned that op. to Dr. Graham," said Zorba smoothly. "No disrespect to you, Ben—but, well, I'm giving the orders and I guess I have every right to expect my staff to obey them. Even Dr. Ben Casey!"

Ben nursed the angle of his powerful jaw.

"You really mean that, don't you?" he asked quietly.

"Yes, Ben, I do. Now then, it's Saturday morning—why not take a trip up to Lake Talla and put in some nice quiet fishing, huh?"

For a moment it almost seemed as if Casey was going to defy Zorba. But he *was* a mite tired—he knew that himself—and perhaps a few days fishing up at Lake Talla might go far to restore the Casey metabolism.

Ben grinned faintly as he realized that such was his preoccupation with medicine that he even thought in medical terms. Still, it was true enough.

"Okay, Dr. Zorba—you win," he said.

"You really mean that, Ben?"

"Yeah, I guess you've sold me on the idea."

Dr. Zorba chuckled. "I must admit that I . . . er, anticipated having quite a battle to persuade you," he said. He put out a hand. "I'm glad you've agreed, Ben," he said. "You'll be all the better for the rest."

"I'll bring you the biggest fish in Lake Talla, Doctor!"

Dr. Zorba's eyes twinkled. "Is that a promise?" he asked.

"Well," grinned Ben, "it's a declaration of intentions, anyway!"

He was pulling the knot of his tie higher up when Dr. Zorba said: "I almost forgot—some mail came this morning regarding the Mallory Foundation."

The Mallory Foundation was a medical organization in which Ben had lately become very interested. It seemed to him that the Foundation, by setting aside new funds for neurosurgical research, was doing a great and needed

job and Ben was extremely anxious to assist in every way open to him.

"What's the letter say?" he inquired.

Zorba coughed. "They have a meeting Sunday evening . . ." he began.

"That settles it!" cried Ben. "I'm not going up to Lake Talla."

"Now look here Ben. . . ."

"I can't be gone fishing when important neurosurgical matters are coming on the agenda," argued Ben.

Dr. Zorba shifted his weight impatiently. "Will you just *listen*, Ben?" he demanded.

"Okay, then—shoot."

"Knowing your keen interest in this fine cause I'm going to send a deputy and one who

I think will be at least a reasonable stand-in for Dr. Ben Casey, M.D."

"You mean Dr. Graham or. . . ."

"I'm sending Dr. David Zorba," replied Dr. David Zorba. He held up a hand. "And no arguments, young man—this is final!"

* * *

So it came to pass that along about four-thirty that afternoon a rakish convertible loaded with fishing-tackle and driven by a handsome, powerfully built young doctor came to rest on the shores of beautiful Lake Talla.

Dr. Ben Casey sighed appreciatively. The sun was still shining brilliantly, the warm air was alive with gracious summer scents, and he was forced to admit that already he was starting to feel better, sort of relaxed and content. Yes, he really *did* need a small vacation and even a few days away from the strain of almost non-stop hospital duties must surely do him good!

He drove on and turned into the main driveway of Lake Talla Lodge, the fine old guesthouse where he would be staying.

He had unpacked and was sauntering out with his rods and gear when he almost bumped into a tall, greying man with a tanned face who was evidently also on his way for a little fishing.

"I'm sorry," said Ben. "I didn't notice you for a second."

The other smiled. "That's all right, no harm done," he replied. He eyed Ben closely. "I do believe we've met . . . no, I've seen your picture in some paper, I think. Aren't you Dr. Casey from 59 West?"

Ben nodded.

"I'm very happy to meet you, Doctor," the other went on. "My name is Alton—John Jesse Alton."

They shook hands and Ben said curiously: "What paper did you see my picture in, Mr. Alton? I wasn't aware the newspapers took that much interest in medical affairs."

"Oh, some paper or other," Alton rejoined. "As a matter of fact, I'm not from your city— my home is in Cranton."

"Cranton? That's a mighty long way off," said Ben. "I just can't imagine how any paper there would even have heard of me. . . ."

"Well, one sure did," said Alton with a smile. He hesitated, then went on: "Perhaps we could do our fishing together, Doctor? We'd be company for each other, eh?"

"Why not?" answered Ben. He laughed. "We can console one another if neither of us gets a strike!"

"There is that aspect of the matter," said Alton.

But there was no need for consolation. By nightfall both had made several considerable catches—a discussion of which kept them in animated chat throughout dinner and the rest of the evening.

In fact, by this time Ben was altogether pleased that he hadn't resisted Dr. Zorba's order to be gone fishing!

"I guess we should meet again in the morning, Doctor, if that's agreeable to you?" said Alton, as he lit a cigar.

"Surely. You want to start early?"

"Well, now an early breakfast—say at seven o'clock—and then off to the fishing grounds, eh?" smiled Alton.

"You've got yourself a date, Mr. Alton."

Ben went up to his room, took a shower and climbed into his pyjamas. He was feeling pleasantly relaxed and yet extraordinarily fit as he got into bed and switched off the light.

It was more than two hours later when he awoke with a curious sensation that there was someone standing motionless within feet of him!

For a moment which seemed like an age he lay unmoving, letting his narrowed eyes probe every area of the room.

Then, quite suddenly, the moon drifted from behind a thick bank of clouds—and sent a shaft of lunar radiance straight into the room.

It lit up a tall, dark figure—whose entire head and shoulders were hidden in a sinister-looking hood!

Ben swung powerfully sideways and in a flash was lunging across the room to come to grips with the hooded terror!

But with a strangled cry the macabre man had wheeled and was through the door and streaking for the fire stairs.

Bent went after him like a bolt from the blue, but on bare feet the going was tough—and tougher still when the sole of his left foot was pierced by a splinter which felt as long as a dagger!

"Ouch!" gasped Ben as pain speared his flesh.

But he panted gamely on. Then, as he neared the door leading to the fire stairs, there was a slamming noise—and the door shut, refusing all attempts to wrench it open.

Ben raced back to his room, donned slippers and went fast down the main stairs into the foyer.

The desk clerk, a small, balding man with a

celluloid collar and a black shoestring tie, looked up over rimless bifocals.

The startled sound which proceeded from him suggested that he found the spectacle of a rushing guest clad only in pyjamas a somewhat unusual, even sensational apparition!

"Wh . . . wh . . . what . . . I mean . . . why . . . what . . ." he babbled.

"Somebody wearing a hood got into my room, I'm after him," shouted Ben as he went through the swing doors and started round the back of the guest-house.

He reached the base of the fire stairs within seconds.

But there was no sign of the mysterious intruder.

Ben hunted around in the grounds, but without success. In the end he had to abandon the search and return to the foyer, where the little middle-aged clerk was waiting with his eyes still popping behind his spectacles.

"D . . . did you catch him, sir?" he quavered—unnecessarily.

"I guess he got clean away," said Ben ruefully. He reached for the telephone. "Better call the police, anyway," he added.

"The local sheriff lives ten miles from here and his car broke down this afternoon," the clerk mentioned sadly.

Ben let the receiver slide back. "Looks like everything is against us," he said. "Will you phone him in the morning?"

"Yes, sir, I'll do that—first thing."

"Maybe he'll be able to get his car going and come out, though I reckon there isn't much he can do." Ben rumpled his hair. "I imagine the intruder just went into the first room he saw, must've been looking for anything handy to steal. . . ."

The clerk nodded. "I expect that would be it, sir," he added.

"You haven't heard of any intruders around these parts, have you?" queried Ben.

"No, sir—everything here is usually kinda peaceful." The clerk made a wry grin. "It's just one of those things it wasn't Mr. Alton who was surprised, sir. . . ."

"Yeah—how so?"

"Mr. Alton originally had your room," the clerk explained. "He only had it changed today, after you booked in on long-distance, sir."

"Oh?" Ben shrugged and went on up to his room. He was clambering back between the sheets when it occurred to him to wonder if the intruder had really thought he was in Jesse Alton's room.

But, of course, that was just imagining things, he told himself before he went off to sleep again.

*   *   *

He mentioned the incident next morning, though, when he and Alton set out on their fishing expedition—and was instantly intrigued by the oddly tense look which crossed the other's suntanned features.

"A man with a hood, eh?" Alton said musingly. "You sure you didn't catch even a fleeting glimpse of his face, Doctor?"

Ben shook his head. "There wasn't a loop-hole—except for the eye-slits," he replied. "Why?"

Alton appeared to hesitate. It was fully half a minute before he answered. Then he said slowly: "I own and run a large trucking business, Doctor. A week ago I had to fire my office manager whom I discovered had been falsifying the accounts—literally helping himself to the company's money."

"I see."

"A man named Pete Boone—a tall fellow with a long white scar running down the left side of his face," went on Alton. "He . . . well, the fact is he made some rather wild threats of personal violence, said he'd get even with me if if was the last thing he did. I was just wondering. . . ."

"Would he know you were on a vacation trip here, Mr. Alton?" asked Ben quietly.

Alton nodded. "Oh, yes—everybody in the office knew. It would be the easiest thing for him to ascertain the name of the guest-house. . . ."

"Maybe even the room number?" suggested Ben.

"What d'you mean?" Alton's eyes flickered. "Of course, I see—I switched my room. He wouldn't know that—but if he had access to office data he would likely know the original room number, for my secretary noted it on a pad! Why, good heavens—that's why he entered your room!"

"Exactly," answered Ben. "He figured I was you . . . I guess it's lucky I woke up in time."

Alton gestured. "It's a terrible thing—why,

he might have done you some injury!" he cried.

Ben grinned faintly. "Well, he didn't get the chance, so we won't worry about it. The local sheriff has been informed—and it's my guess this hooded fellow won't dare risk coming back to the hotel."

"I hope not, I most certainly hope not," re-joined Alton.

"Well, it's no use spoiling our day worrying," said Ben. He went down a mossy slope to the lovely shore of the lake with lines of tall trees ranged round it. "This sure looks a likely spot," he remarked. "Shall we fish here for a while?"

Alton nodded. "Yes, I believe this section has some very fine rainbow trout," he said.

They fished for two hours, making several good strikes.

Alton stretched himself and then said: "I think I'll try a little farther along, Doctor—farther up, just round that bend. You joining me?"

Ben looked down at his catch. "I guess I'm doing so well right here that I'd be foolish to change, Mr. Alton," he said. "But I'll move along in your direction later."

"Right—see you presently then," answered Alton. And, gathering up his rods and tackle, he sauntered along the sandy shore until he was lost to view behind massive twin boulders.

Ben waded out a little, expertly casting another fly. There was a plop—but this time he just missed making a strike. He brought the rod back in and was getting ready to cast again when a series of thudding sounds assailed his ears, followed by a choking cry.

In an instant Ben had dropped his rod and was racing along the shore.

As he rounded the bend marked by the boulders he pulled up. For lying almost at his feet was the prostrate figure of John Jesse Alton.

He was spreadeagled on his side, both arms outflung, and Ben knew at once that his head had been injured.

"Maybe he slipped and fell headlong," he told himself. He glanced upwards. The slope was not steep and its surface was soft. It seemed improbable that . . . he shrugged, realizing that his immediate task was medical and not one of detection as to how his new friend came to fall.

He went down on one knee, starting his examination.

"Mmmm . . . depressed skull fracture," Ben muttered. "I hope it isn't complicated by intracranial haemorrhage. . . ."

He made Alton comfortable, covering him with his own jacket, and hesitated. As a doctor, he knew the risk of carrying an injured and shocked person—on the other hand, he hesitated to leave him while going for assistance.

He glanced again at the slope. It just didn't seem possible for Alton to have gotten a fracture merely by rolling down that soft undulation. . . .

Then, out of the corner of his eye, he detected a flashing movement in the dense undergrowth along the shore itself.

Someone was creeping through the brush, nearer and nearer!

An idea came swiftly into Ben's agile mind. He made an exaggerated shrug and said aloud: "Well, I guess I'll just have to leave him while I go back to the guest-house for a stretcher!"

And he turned and stalked off, round the bend—then immediately stopped and crept softly back.

A man hooded and in black emerged into the open. In his hand was a jagged section of rock.

"Guess I'll jest finish yuh off, Alton!" he exulted. "Yuh didn't get the full impact up on the slope. This time I. . . ."

The words froze on his mouth as Dr. Ben Casey leaped straight into view, both fists swinging!

"Ow . . . ug . . . ow. . . ." With a wild yelp the hooded terror bounded back—to go slithering down the mossy bank straight into the deep blue water of the shimmering lake.

Sp . . . lash!

Awk!

Zunk!

The hooded head vanished below the surface, then came up. The arms started cleaving the water.

In a fraction of a second Ben grabbed Alton's fallen rod—and made what he afterwards rated as the best cast of a lifetime!

The hook ripped into the sinister one's hood, tearing it wide open—and there was a white, ravaged face with a long scar running down the left cheek!

Ben hauled on the line while the other struggled frantically. Then Ben picked up a long-handled net and, reaching out, clamped it with a wham over the luckless attacker's head!

Bim! Blap!

With a movement of his powerful wrists Ben hauled the attacker to shore, reached out a hand and yanked him sprawling on to the bank. It was the work of a moment to secure the other's hands with strong fishing twine.

"Mister Pete Boone, I presume?" said Ben amiably.

Maddened eyes glared up at him, but no words came from Boone's twitching mouth. So far as he was concerned the war was over!

*   *   *

It was an hour later.

Jesse Alton was in bed in his room, Ben was sitting by him and the villainous Pete Boone was in the sheriff's wagon *en route* for the county jailhouse.

A hurry call to the local doctor had brought the latter along post haste with his equipment, but it was Ben Casey who went to work on Alton.

The depressed fracture was ugly, but less serious than might have been expected, as Ben's detailed analysis showed. Best of all there were no complications, like intracranial bleeding.

Doc Morgan had watched Ben with undisguised admiration.

"Heard about your work at 59 West," he offered. "I can tell now that what I heard was no exaggeration."

"Well, I guess Alton'll be all right," responded Ben. "But as soon as possible I think it would be better to get him into hospital where he can be under constant observation, especially during the preliminary stages."

Dr. Morgan nodded. "I'll arrange all that, Casey," he said. He held out a gnarled hand. "It's been both a professional and a personal pleasure meeting you," he added handsomely.

Ben completed his vacation and drove back to 59 West four days later. Alton had regained consciousness and was, Ben could see, likely to make a quite rapid recovery in his local hospital.

When Ben got out of his car at 59 West the first man he ran into was Dr. Zorba.

"So even on a fishing trip you just can't keep your nose out of matters medical, eh?" said Zorba.

Ben grinned. "I don't know how you come to have heard . . ." he began.

Dr. Zorba's eyes twinkled again. "Darn it, your fame seems to spread everywhere," he said. "I got a phone call on behalf of Alton—and this letter came for you by special delivery an hour ago."

Ben took the long slim envelope and slit it open. Something fell out. It was a cheque for five thousand dollars!

There was a note, apparently written with some slight difficulty. It was from Alton and read:

My dear Casey,

For all you did please accept the attached cheque for whatever purpose you may wish to apply it, though I guess I already know what it will be. You see, I saw your photo in a medical journal which reported your great interest in the work of the Mallory Foundation. And if you're wondering how I come to have read medical journals, the answer is that my son is Dr. Frank L. Alton, a neurosurgeon at Cranton Hospital. I was going to tell you about him when I was attacked. Then I thought this might be an even better way.

Yours as always,
John Jesse Alton.

Ben smote a knee. "Young Frank Alton. . . . I remember now, I saw *his* name in the journal," he said. "But, darn it, I just didn't connect the son with the father. . . ."

"No reason why you should make a medical connection, was there, Ben?" murmured Dr. Zorba.

"I . . . well, I suppose not."

"I mean you just *wouldn't* be thinking of medicine when you'd gone fishing, would you?" asked Dr. Zorba innocently.

"Well. . . ."

"You don't even have to think of the subject . . . it just tramps in on Dr. Ben Casey, no matter where he is," chuckled Dr. Zorba.

THOUGH IT WAS DR. DAN DAZZLER'S DAY OFF, THE SHRIEK OF AN AMBULANCE SIREN QUICKLY BROUGHT HIM BACK TO DUTY. HELPING TO PATCH THE TEEN-AGE VICTIMS OF A VICIOUS GANG FIGHT, THE YOUNG INTERNE FOUND HIMSELF SUDDENLY FACE-TO-FACE WITH THE STARK TERROR OF A ....

RUMBLE..!

42

AND SO, A SHORT TIME LATER, AT THE NINETY-SECOND PRECINCT...

B-BUT YOU'VE **GOT** TO BELIEVE ME! I'M DR. DAN DAZZLER, INTERNE AT...

LOOK, KID... IT'S A GOOD TRY, BUT NO SOAP! YOU'RE MUCH TOO YOUNG TO BE A DOCTOR, YOU'RE NOT IN UNIFORM, YOU LOOK LIKE YOU LED THE CHARGE UP SAN JUAN HILL... AND YOU'RE WOUNDED LIKE ALL YOUR PALS! NOW HOW ABOUT SETTLING DOWN AND GETTING BACK INTO LINE WITH YOUR PLAYMATES?

SOME KID'S GOT A WOUND THAT'S RE-OPENED, SARGE! LOOKS NASTY... BETTER CALL A DOCTOR!

I'M A DOCTOR! GOT A FIRST AID KIT, HERE? BRING IT... AND HURRY!

RELUCTANTLY, THE POLICE LET DAN GO TO WORK. IN A FEW MINUTES...

THERE! **THAT** SHOULD HOLD!

S-SOMETHING TELLS ME WE MAY HAVE MADE A SLIGHT MISTAKE, OFFICER CLAGHORN. HE **STILL** LOOKS LIKE ONE OF THESE YOUNG PUNKS! BUT HE'S A **MEDIC** ALL RIGHT!

I - I THINK WE'D BETTER CHECK WITH THAT HOSPITAL WHERE YOU SAY YOU WORK. I STILL HAVE MY DOUBTS ABOUT WHO...

LOOK WHAT I JUST FOUND ON ONE OF THOSE KIDS, SARGE! IT'S A WALLET HE MUST'VE SWIPED... FROM A **DR. DANIEL DAZZLER!** SAYS HE FOUND IT IN AN OLD COAT...

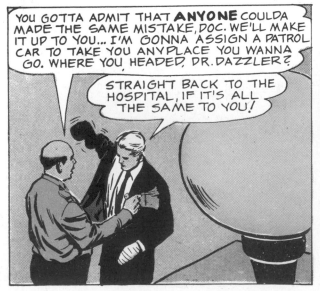

YOU GOTTA ADMIT THAT **ANYONE** COULDA MADE THE SAME MISTAKE, DOC. WE'LL MAKE IT UP TO YOU... I'M GONNA ASSIGN A PATROL CAR TO TAKE YOU ANYPLACE YOU WANNA GO. WHERE YOU HEADED, DR. DAZZLER?

STRAIGHT BACK TO THE HOSPITAL, IF IT'S ALL THE SAME TO YOU!

B-BACK TO THE **HOSPITAL?** BUT... BUT YOU JUST SAID YOU WERE OFF-DUTY! WHY'RE YOU GOING BACK TO THE HOSP...?

IT'S **HEALTHIER** THERE... AND A LOT **SAFER!** SO LONG!

The Vanishing PATIENT

IT was a free night for Dr. Ben Casey and only that morning an invitation had come for him to dine with Perry Lester and his wife Larraine at their new bungalow on Riverside Boulevard.

Perry was an attorney whom Ben had come to know quite well as a result of an automobile accident in which Perry had been linked legally.

Both Perry and Larraine had become close friends of the famous medico at 59 West and Ben knew he would have a very pleasant evening.

But the invitation clashed with a committee meeting in connection with the coming Neurosurgical Convention, so Ben had regretfully turned the invitation down.

"I hope you're not offended, Perry," he said over the phone.

A chuckle came down the wire.

"We're disappointed," said Perry, "but both Larraine and I know all about your almost total devotion to medicine, even out of hospital hours. . . ."

"A good medic doesn't keep hospital hours, I guess," said Ben. "I just have to be at the committee meeting, Perry. A number of important things are coming up and they'll expect me to join in the discussion. But, I'll tell you what —if the meeting finishes not too late I could drop around for coffee and a chat."

"Great, you do that, Ben," rejoined Perry. "I'll tell Larraine we may expect you later, then?"

"Sure—and if I don't keep the date you can bet it won't be my fault."

Nor was it—though Ben could never have dreamed of the strange turn events were to take.

It was around nine-fifteen in the evening when the meeting finished.

"Plenty of time to drop around at Perry's place," reflected Ben as he went out for his car. It was dark on the street and he had got the car door opened before he received his first shock.

A man was lying slumped over the steering-wheel!

As Ben stood there staring, footsteps came up behind him and, wheeling, he saw that the newcomer was Dr. Frank Malling, who had also been at the meeting.

"Say, Ben, what's wrong?" inquired Malling.

"I just found this man lying in my car, Frank." As he spoke, Ben was already conducting a swift and incisive preliminary examination.

"Funny," he said. "No sign of concussion, no smell of intoxicants." He bent closer, moving his skilled hands. He continued the examination for a few more minutes, then said in an odd voice: "Frank—it looks like this guy is *drugged*!"

"Drugged—are you sure?"

"Not completely so, Frank—but all the signs point that way. It's my guess this fellow was feeling bad and more or less fell into the car— maybe he figured it was safer there."

"Safer than he'd know," mused Malling. "I mean he couldn't know it was Ben Casey's automobile!"

"Well, there's only one thing to do—I'd better get him to 59 West without delay."

Ben gently moved the prostrate man, covered him with a rug, and then slid down behind the wheel himself.

In a few moments Ben was driving hard and fast for the hospital. He arrived without further incident.

"Thought you were having the evening off, Ben . . ." began Dr. David Zorba. Then, his eyes taking in the scene fully, he said: "Trouble certainly seems to go out of its way to find you! What happened, Ben?"

Briefly but lucidly, Ben explained—and in another moment the unconscious man was being wheeled into the emergency ward.

"I'm pretty certain he doesn't need surgery," Ben said. "It looks like drugs. . . ."

Zorba's eyebrows rose.

"You mean he's a junky—a drug addict?"

Ben grinned faintly. "I wouldn't like to say at this stage," he answered. "I might have a better idea when I've applied all the appropriate tests."

A quarter of an hour later Ben had completed his detailed examination—and made his diagnosis.

"I'm willing to say right now that this man is no addict," he announced. "It looks a clear case of injection—with pentathol!"

"You don't say?"

Ben nodded. "I never heard of an addict injecting himself with *that*," he said. "This man has been deliberately anaesthetized!"

Dr. Zorba's face wore a worried look.

"If you're right—and I never doubt your diagnoses, though sometimes your methods strike us as just a little unorthodox—then this looks like a case for the police," he declared.

"Yeah," said Ben heavily. "I guess I'll call them right away."

He was reaching for the telephone when Zorba said slowly: "You know, Ben, the extraordinary thing is that a man injected with pentathol should be able to get into your car— especially if he was *forcibly* injected!"

"There'd be very little time before the shot acted on him," agreed Ben. He nursed the side of his jaw and added: "There are things about this which just don't make sense. Well, I guess that's police work, Doctor."

He made the call and strolled out of the emergency room chatting with Zorba.

"There's nothing I can do for this fellow before the police show up," he said. "We'll just have to wait for him to regain consciousness and tell us his own story."

They were in Zorba's office when they were informed that Captain Lou Granger had arrived from Police Headquarters.

Granger, a big rangy man pushing forty, listened impassively while Ben related what had occurred.

"Sounds kind of screwy to me, Doc," Granger said. "How long d'you figger it'll be before this guy wakes up?"

Ben glanced at his strap watch. "It's a little hard to assess the time since the shot was administered, Captain," he said, "but we can be strolling back to the emergency ward. The night sister may have news."

Zorba smiled. "If there's even the faintest sign of returning consciousness I reckon you'll spot it yourself," he said.

Together they went to the ward. There was no sign of the pretty young night sister and

Zorba's face hardened, for the disciplinary rules of 59 West were stern and inflexible.

When they reached the bed—it was the only case on emergency that night—Ben pulled up, staring.

For the clothes had been pulled up over the prostrate figure's head.

"What the . . ." began Dr. Zorba angrily.

But Ben had already reached down and pulled the sheets back.

Lying in the bed, bound and tightly gagged, was Sister Lucy Moran!

*   *   *

When they had freed her, Ben gave her some water and the sister managed to find words, though with difficulty.

"Two masked men came in through the fire stairs door and overpowered me," she gasped. "The next thing I knew I was being flung into the bed—while the patient was removed!"

Captain Granger's chin jutted combatively.

"Say, when I get my hands on them hoods I'll——" he rasped.

"No doubt," said Dr. Zorba. "But the way it looks right now we seem to have not the remotest chance of knowing who they were!"

Captain Granger bit on his underlip.

"You're darned right, Doc," he said. "But there must be some way . . . there *must* be!"

Ben Casey hadn't yet spoken. His eyes were roving the immediate vicinity of the bed, as if seeking some clue.

But there was nothing.

"Lucy," he said gently, "was there anything, any small or seemingly insignificant thing, about these men?"

Lucy's blue eyes looked up at him. Her fair head shook slowly.

"Were they tall or short, or did they speak? Anything, Lucy. . . ." He broke off, staring intently.

"There *was* just one thing," Sister Moran said. "But I'd never have recollected it but for your questioning. . . ."

"What is it, Lucy?"

Lucy Moran pushed hair back from her forehead.

"There were two men, like I said, Ben," she resumed. "They were both around average height—maybe five feet nine inches tall. But the one who gagged and bound me bent low—very close to me and I caught a strong smell. It was garlic. . . ."

"Garlic!" Captain Granger rapped the word out. "Say, that could make this guy an Italian!"

"Non-Italians sometimes cook food with garlic," said Ben mildly. "Still, I'll agree it could be helpful." He turned back to Sister Moran, dropping an arm on her shoulder. "Was there anything else, Lucy?"

"No, I . . ."

"Think real hard," said Ben.

"No, nothing, only he wore a ring. Well, I guess a lot of men wear rings. Wait a minute, though. I remember now. It was broken. . . ."

"Broken—how?"

"Broken right across and there was a clip of wire holding it together and . . ."

"Captain, that looks like a real clue," said Zorba slowly.

"Oh, sure," grunted Granger. "All we gotta do is check up on the hands of all the Italians living in the city—I guess there ain't no more than a few thousand!"

"Just the same, it's a clue," said Ben.

"I guess so," said Granger. "Oh, well, I'll get back to Headquarters and start things moving. I'll keep in touch."

"Thanks," said Ben. When the captain had gone he stood for a moment lost in thought. Then the phone jangled. He picked the receiver up. A strange voice moved into his ear—a harsh, rustling voice, like dead leaves blown against rusted wire.

"Doctor Ben Casey?"

"Speaking. Who are you?"

"Don't ask questions, Doc, and don't bother to talk until I say," the voice grated. "This is just to tell you to keep your snooping medical beezer outa business that ain't no business of yours. You got that, Doc?"

"Yeah." Mutely, Ben signalled with his eyes. Then, grabbing a scratch-pad he hastily scrawled: *Get police to check the number calling. Urgent.*

Dr. Zorba read the words, nodded and hurried silently from the room.

"Well, that's all you gotta do, Ben Casey," the strange voice went on. "Just keep your nose clean and nothing ain't gonna happen to you. . . ."

"And if I don't?" said Ben. He was fighting for words, any words, that would keep the mysterious caller on the line long enough for the law to check on the call.

A bitter chuckle greeted him.

"If you don't, then I guess 59 West is sure gonna be short of its bright young medic. . . ."

"You don't scare me, my friend," said Ben grimly.

"You're just talking, Doc—talking to keep me on the line while you check up on the phone I'm using! Heh, heh, heh—it won't do you no good to know, but I'll tell you. I'm phoning from Plaza 08881. A pay telephone booth at Jackson Boulevard and Ninth Street. So long, Doc. . . ." There was another evil chuckle and then a click as the unseen caller slammed the receiver back on its cradle.

Ben Casey streaked through the door and almost leaped into his car. In another minute he was roaring down the roadway. It led directly to the intersection of Jackson and Ninth and there was just the faintest chance that he might be in time to see something.

He was almost there when a long white convertible with the roof up screamed past him, heading in the opposite direction. Ben caught a fleeting glimpse of a dead white face and glittering eyes—and, acting on inspiration, made a fast turn and went after the car.

There were lights ahead showing red, but the convertible jumped them and Ben took the same risk.

But the convertible was going fast and ever faster. Ben's eyes noted his own climbing speedometer . . . sixty-eight, seventy, seventy-seven, eighty-two, ninety!

Now there was less traffic, for they were through the downtown section and heading for the open country and the State Highway.

Ben jammed his foot harder still on the accelerator pedal, and slowly but inexorably the gap between them began to lessen.

Then it happened!

There was a spurt of livid flame and a series of hard, snapping blasts.

Crraaaack!

Zunk!

Blap!

Windscreen glass splintered, but no fragments blinded Ben Casey, for the glass was smash-proof.

There were no more shots. Apparently, the driver was anxious not to slow himself too much by firing.

An idea came to Ben. Deliberately, he allowed the distance between them to widen.

"That'll make him figure he's losing me," thought Ben.

He drove on steadily, still deliberately losing ground, but just keeping the other car barely in view.

Then, suddenly, he rounded an S bend to

find a long stretch of roadway ahead—and not a thing on it!

Ben went down through the gears, his eyes darting every way in the hope of seeing the car. Maybe it had gotten off the highway. It must have, Ben decided, for there was no intersection anywhere in sight.

He put the car into reverse and backed slowly, his eyes questing from one side of the road to the other.

It was a move that brought results.

Around seventy yards farther back, Ben's alert gaze picked out tyre marks as they weaved off the highway and through thick clumps of grass and dotted boulders.

He followed them, driving slowly and with as little sound as he could manage.

The tyre marks were clear enough now and he followed them for a quarter-mile until they disappeared between two huge overhanging trees.

Ben cut his motor and climbed out. Not for the first time, he was playing a hunch—a hunch which told him it might well be better to go on ahead without the betraying sound of his motor.

He moved carefully through the trees. It was very dark now and he had to walk with his hands spread out to feel his way. But there was ample room—after all, the convertible had actually been driven this way—but Ben didn't want to risk sprawling headlong against some unforeseen projection.

He walked this way for all of seven minutes, then pulled up abruptly.

For just ahead of him the trees and undergrowth widened into a clearing—in the centre of which stood the convertible. Its lights were out, but Ben could see it clearly enough—for right ahead of him was a ramshackle log cabin with light glowing from its window.

Moving with the greatest care, Ben weaved his way round the side of the clearing until he was exactly opposite the rear fender of the big convertible.

For a moment he stood utterly still, breathing through his mouth. But no sound came to him and no figure appeared.

He was going towards the log cabin when a sudden thought struck him and he leaned inside the convertible and put a hand into the glove compartment.

A sardonic smile flitted briefly across his lean mouth. For his hand had touched a gun.

He drew the weapon out. It was a ·33 Smith and Wesson, and it was fully loaded. Ben flicked off the safety-catch and darted like a silent shadow for the sheltering side wall of the cabin. He edged slowly along it until he reached a window.

Then, peeping just enough to see inside, he drew his breath in sharply.

The drugged man was lying prone on a bed. Cords bound his feet and shackled them to the bedpost. His hands were spreadeagled and roped, with the hard cord running under the bed.

The prostrate man groaned, then stirred. Slowly, his eyes opened—to stare up at the sinister figure bending over him.

"You . . . you . . ."

"Heh, heh, heh!" The man bent lower. "This time I got you safe, Mister James Loomis! You ain't gonna make a break for it while you're still conscious like you did back in town!" It was the rasping voice Ben had heard over the phone.

"I . . . I . . ." The shackled man swallowed painfully. "What . . . what do . . ."

"What do I want? I'll tell you. Just your name on a nice document . . . a cheque for fifty thousand dollars made payable to me and a personal note to your bank saying it's to be paid in cash, pronto!"

"Fifty thousand . . . you must be crazy!"

"I was never more sane, my friend," said the other.

The prostrate man stared pallidly.

"Know you now. . . . Why, you're the man I saw talking to my office manager the other day when . . . why . . . why. . . ." An incredulous look came on his face.

"Yeah, that's right, you've seen me. Jake Horgan is the name. Yeah, you seen me talking with Carlo Mansetti, your manager."

"Then . . . then . . ."

"You're getting with it, dad," cackled Horgan. "Yeah, it was Carlo was dreamed-up the idea. Twenty-five grand apiece we get . . . *if* you want to go on living!"

"I'll never . . ."

Horgan sneered. "Don't kid yourself, Loomis," he said. "Carlo can be *very* unpleasant when guys try to act tough with him."

He turned the sneer into another cackle. "Carlo couldn't risk being seen in it himself—but he provided the means. See?" So speaking, Horgan whipped out a hypodermic. "That's how we drugged you—or, rather, I did. But Carlo gave me the hypo. Unfortunately, you ran out of your car when I leaned over from the back and plugged you with the needle. Heh, heh, heh—it was one smart play toppling into Doctor Ben Casey's old heap. But we got you outa that hospital as easy as could be . . . and this time you ain't got even the ghost of a chance!"

Loomis strained madly at his bonds, but to no avail.

"Keep struggling, Loomis—it ain't gonna do you no good," said Horgan. "Now I'll just get your cheque-book out and untie your writing-hand . . . heh, heh, heh!"

Ben Casey flattened himself farther against the wall of the cabin, for he had heard the smallest sound in the distance. The sound grew and in another moment a car entered the clearing—but from a different direction.

Ben breathed in relief. The newcomer must be Carlo. It was fortunate he had not driven the same way!

The motor stopped and a dark figure with glistening black hair and a pencil-line moustache shouldered through the door.

Ben peeped back through the side window.

Carlo swung into the room—and in his hand was a long Colt revolver!

"Ceiling zero, Horgan," he jeered.

Horgan wheeled with a strangled cry.

"You . . . you . . . you ain't . . ." he babbled.

A thin twisted smile ravaged Mansetti's face.

"*Si*," he whispered. "*Si, signor* . . . now I get the cheque all to myself and leave you with our friend Signor Loomis."

"You . . . you're giving me the double-cross!" croaked Horgan.

Mansetti nodded. "That's-a right, *signor*. How you like that, huh?"

"I'll get you for this!" screeched Horgan.

"*Lei si sbaglia*," said Mansetti. He grinned. "Ah, you no onnerstan' *italiano*, no? Okay, I tell you in good *inglese*—you are mistaken. You an't gonna get me—now or any time." A chuckle escaped from him. "By the time you and Signor Loomis get free, Carlo will be in sunny Italy! Haw, haw, haw!"

With a wild cry, Loomis plunged sideways. There was a crack from the gun.

Zunk . . . wheeeee!

The bullet ripped into the side window. Glass flew out—and Ben poked his own gun in, waiting.

But before he could act, Mansetti brought the butt of his gun down hard on Horgan's neck. There was a dull thud as he rolled over and lay still.

Carlo Mansetti laughed mirthlessly. He went over to the bed.

"And now, Signor Loomis, you sign the leetle piece of so-valuable paper, *si*?" His eyes hardened. "Is best you no make the trouble, eh?"

Mansetti was standing now with his back to the shattered window. Unhurriedly, Ben stepped

through. He knew Loomis had seen him and he only hoped the latter did not betray this knowledge with his eyes.

Slowly and deliberately, Ben bent low and came up with the hypodermic. He moved swiftly then—and in the next second the needle had jabbed Mansetti's forearm where his shirt sleeve had ridden up.

Mansetti let out a stricken cry, then wheeled, his eyes glaring balefully at Ben.

He brought the gun up with a convulsive jerk, but Ben slammed it from his grasp and the big weapon thudded across the pinewood floor.

Then a glazed look came in Mansetti's eyes. His lips moved, but no sound came from them.

Ben caught him as he toppled.

Something that was almost a chuckle came to him from the bed.

"Poetic justice, that, Doc," said Loomis.

*   *   *

Ben looked at his watch again. It was twenty minutes past eleven p.m.

He had taken Loomis to hospital for a medical check-up and had taken Mansetti and Horgan to Police Headquarters. The police surgeon could check on the rascally Horgan!

Ben ran his car across the gravelled drive in front of the bungalow.

"Why, Ben!" cried Larraine. "How nice to see you, after all—we'd really given you up!"

"Come right on in," said Perry heartily. "You're in nice time for some hot coffee, and I think Larraine has some very tasty rolls still awaiting you!"

"I could eat them all right," said Ben with a grin.

They went into the spacious lounge.

"How did the meeting go, Ben?" asked Larraine.

"The meeting?"

"Well, of course."

"Oh, the *meeting*?" grinned Ben. "It was the most successful I've attended."

"Plenty of neurosurgical talk, eh?"

"Something like that."

"Do you give practical demonstrations, Ben?" asked Perry curiously.

"I did tonight, anyway," said Ben with another grin.

IT STARTED AS A DELIGHTFULLY FESTIVE OCCASION... A FROLICSOME EVENING DEVOTED TO LIGHT-HEARTED CELEBRATION OF DR. DAVID ZORBA'S BIRTHDAY. BUT LESS THAN AN HOUR LATER UNEXPECTED EVENTS BEGAN TO TAKE PLACE IN THE OPULENT CLUB PERISCOPE. BEFORE ANYONE COULD INTERFERE, THE HARMLESS SCUFFLE AT A NEARBY TABLE HAD EXPLODED INTO A SAVAGE FIGHT... AND BEN CASEY AND HIS FRIENDS BECAME HELPLESS EYEWITNESSES TO....

EYEWITNESS

THIS IS ALMOST INDECENT, BEN CASEY! THE ATTENTION YOU, TED AND MAGGIE ARE SHOWERING ON ME BRINGS A BLUSH TO THESE FADED OLD CHEEKS. I... FEEL LIKE A YOUNG BRIDE BEING WHISKED TO THE ALTAR.

THIS OCCASION IS FAR RARER THAN A MERE WEDDING, DR. ZORBA!

ACCORDING TO STATISTICS, BLUSHING BRIDES ARE BEING MARRIED CONSTANTLY. BUT THE GREAT DR. DAVID ZORBA CELEBRATES HIS NATAL DAY BUT ONCE A... SAY, JUST WHEN **DID** YOU LAST ADMIT TO A BIRTHDAY?

MY **BIRTHDAY?** IS **THAT** WHY WE'RE HERE, ALL DECKED OUT IN SOUP-AND-FISH? SOMETHING ELSE HAS PUZZLED ME, TOO. HOW DID YOU ARRANGE TIME-OFF SO THAT ALL FOUR OF US COULD...?

DON'T ANSWER... I'D RATHER NOT KNOW! I'M SURE YOUR METHODS WERE SO IN-GENIOUS THAT THEY'D SHOCK THESE INNOCENT EARS. ONE QUESTION, THOUGH... HOW **DID** YOU FIND OUT THIS IS MY BIRTHDAY? HYPNOSIS? **TRUTH SERUM?**

REMEMBER MR. ZONDO, THE BEARDED PATIENT WHO CLAIMED HE WAS TOO OLD AND TIRED TO GO ON LIVING? RE-CALL HOW YOU BOOSTED HIS MORALE?

CERTAINLY...BY TELLING HIM I WAS AT LEAST 10 YEARS OLDER THAN **HE** WAS. BY SHOWING HIM THAT A MAN OF MY AGE COULD STILL BE FULL OF ZEST AND LIMIT-LESS CHARM.

PRECISELY! AND BEING FROM MISSOURI, MR. ZONDO DEMANDED PROOF OF YOUR AGE... A PEEK AT YOUR BIRTH CERTIFICATE. YOUR THERAPY. WORKED LIKE A CHARM!

IF I'D KNOWN ZONDO WAS A BLABBERMOUTH I PROBABLY WOULDN'T HAVE HELPED THAT HIRSUTE HIPPO!

NOW THAT YOU KNOW MY SECRET, IS **THIS** TO BE MY PUNISHMENT? A VISIT TO THIS...THIS AQUARIUM?

PERHAPS YOU'RE RIGHT, DR. ZORBA. IT'S DOWNRIGHT CRIMINAL TO ASK A MAN OF YOUR SENSITIVITY. TO DINE AT A PLACE LIKE CLUB PERISCOPE...

CLUB PERISCOPE

...WE'D BETTER GO SOMEWHERE ELSE. HOW ABOUT THE CAFETERIA AT "59 WEST"?

UGGHHH! SUDDENLY THIS PLACE LOOKS LIKE A DELIGHTFUL OASIS!

WE'LL LEAVE THE ORDERING OF THIS DELECTABLE MEAL TO DR. ZORBA... WHOSE CENTENNIAL WE'RE CELEBRATING TONIGHT. MR. ZONDO SUGGESTS...

ZONDO, AGAIN? WHAT'S THAT BEARDED BLIMP GOT TO DO WITH THIS LITTLE ORGY? SAY, IF YOU DON'T MIND MY INQUISITIVENESS, HAS ONE OF YOU COMMITTED GRAND LARCENY IN ORDER TO FINANCE THIS AFFAIR? WHO'S FOOTING THE BILL...?

I AM, DAVID ZORBA! I THOUGHT IT APPROPRIATE THAT AN OLD PIRATE LIKE ME SHOULD BRING SOME CHEER INTO THE DRAB LIFE OF A DECREPIT WITCH DOCTOR LIKE YOU!

Z-ZEBEDIAH ZONDO! WHAT ARE YOU DOING HERE, DECKED OUT LIKE SOMETHING FROM H.M.S. PINAFORE?

ARE YOU EMPLOYED AS A SHILL FOR THIS PLACE, ZEBEDIAH? THAT TENT YOU'RE WEARING... AND THAT HEADGEAR!

ALL A PART OF THE THERAPY YOU SUGGESTED WHILE I WAS YOUR PATIENT. FOLLOWING YOUR ADVICE, I'VE BEGUN TO LIVE AGAIN!

THE CLUB PERISCOPE IS MINE... I OWN THE WHOLE SHEBANG! THIS LITTLE PARTY IN YOUR HONOUR IS JUST A TOKEN OF MY GENUINE ADMIRATION, YOU ANCIENT MARINER! ANY OTHER QUESTIONS?

JUST ONE, ZEBEDIAH. WHAT TIME DOES THIS PLUSH-LINED BATHYSPHERE OF YOURS SUBMERGE?

HAW HAW!! YOU OLD BUZZARD... **ALL** OF YOU...... EAT HEARTY!

WHEN THE LAVISH MEAL IS COMPLETED...

NOW THAT YOU'RE TOO BLOATED TO GET UP AND RUN AWAY, DR. ZORBA... WE'VE TRAPPED YOU INTO ACCEPTING THIS LITTLE DOODAD FROM SURGICAL STAFF AT "59 WEST"!

T-THIS RIBBON IS KNOTTED SO TIGHT THAT I CAN'T...

IF YOU WERE EVER SO FUMBLE-FINGERED IN SURGERY YOU'D GET SACKED. BETTER LET MAGGIE DO THE HONOURS.

IT... IT'S MAGNIFICENT! I-I'M COMPLETELY AT A LOSS FOR WORDS...

WHICH PROVES THERE'S A FIRST TIME FOR EVERYTHING! SOMETHING WRONG WITH YOUR EYE, DR. ZORBA?

A... A CINDER MUST'VE GOTTEN INTO IT. T-THIS IS JUST WHAT I'VE ALWAYS DREAMED OF OWNING... WHAT **IS** IT? A PORTABLE UNIVAC?

IT'S A SPECIAL CHRONOGRAPH. A STOP-WATCH, A TACHOMETER, A POCKET ALARM CLOCK, AND THIS IS A...

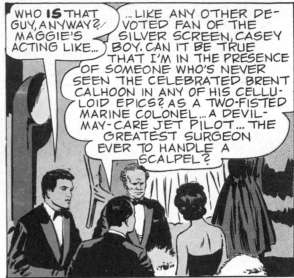

AT THE CALHOON' TABLE THE MEAL IS SERVED AND...

KAREN, DOES THIS TASTE... WELL...UNDISTINGUISHED?

NO MORE SO THAN THIS GLOP **EVER** DOES, MAN OF NATURE. HOW I LONG FOR THOSE DAYS WHEN YOU WERE PREPARING FOR THE PART OF THE WORLD'S GREATEST GOURMET, BARON VON ESSEN!

SUDDENLY...

MY PERFORMANCE AS VON ESSEN **WAS** RATHER MEMORABLE, WASN'T IT?

SNAP! SNAP!

THIS SLOP...CLEAR IT AWAY IMMEDIATELY! BRING, INSTEAD, A STEAMING TUREEN OF MOCK TURTLE SOUP... AND BE CERTAIN THE CREATURES WERE NO MORE THAN SIX MONTHS OLD.

DARLING, YOU'RE PRICELESS!

HURRYING BACK, THE WAITER STARTS TO SERVE THEM...

HEY! YOU THINK THESE STUFFED-SHIRTS MIGHT GET A CHARGE OUT OF THAT ROUGH-TOUGH LUMBERJACK I DID IN "STRONGEST MAN IN THE WORLD"?

I-I DON'T THINK THIS IS THE PLACE OR THE TIME, DEAR...

WATCH OUT, YOU STUPID RUMMY!

OOOOOOO!!

I... I'M TERRIBLY SORRY, LADY! ISH THERE ANY-THING I CAN DO TO HELP?

SURE THERE IS, YOU LUSH! **BEAT IT!**

SPLASHHH!

THANKS, PAL! THAT WAS LIKE A COLD SHOWER... OR TAKING AN EIGHT-COUNT. CLEARED ALL THE COWBWEBS FROM THE OLD SKULL! NOW WE CAN SQUARE ACCOUNTS, EH?

STAY AWAY FROM ME, LITTLE MAN! I-I'M WARNING YOU... GET ME ANGRY AND I'LL DRY-MOD THE FLOOR WITH YOU!

SOUNDS LIKE WORDS RIGHT OUT OF YOUR LAST PICTURE! YOU'LL NEED MORE THAN THAT TO HELP YOU THIS TIME, THESPIAN! THINK YOU CAN SHOVE JACK GATLING AROUND, DO YOU?

KEEP... AWAY...!

THIS IS GONNA BE A NEW EXPERIENCE FOR YOU, CALHOON... A LOT DIFFERENT FROM THOSE PHONY SCREEN FIGHTS YOU ALWAYS WIN!

SOMONE ... STOP THEM! PLEASE!

UGHHH!

THWUNKK!

THE PATIENT IS QUICKLY PREPPED, THEN...

IS OUR PATIENT READY, MAGGIE?

READY AS HE'LL EVER BE, BEN.

LET'S SEE WHAT WE CAN DO FOR MR. GATLING. NURSE... START THE CLOCK!

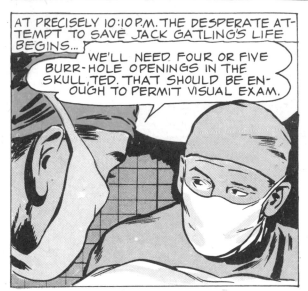

AT PRECISELY 10:10 P.M. THE DESPERATE ATTEMPT TO SAVE JACK GATLING'S LIFE BEGINS...

WE'LL NEED FOUR OR FIVE BURR-HOLE OPENINGS IN THE SKULL, TED. THAT SHOULD BE ENOUGH TO PERMIT VISUAL EXAM.

THE MENINGEAL VESSELS ARE BADLY TORN ON THE UNDERSURFACE, BEN...

I WAS AFRAID THEY **WOULD** BE!

MASSIVE DISCOLORATION ON THE SURFACE OF THE BRAIN... BLEEDING FROM THE TINY BLOOD VESSELS...

JUST WHAT I FEARED... SUBDURAL HEMATOMAS. AT LEAST **TWO** OF THEM, TED... MAYBE MORE.

GOT TO REMOVE THOSE CLOTS IMMEDIATELY...

IF WE'RE LUCKY, THEY'LL REMOVE THE PRESSURE ON THE BRAIN!

SLOWLY-THE CLOCK TICKS OFF THE SECONDS, AS THE DESPERATE FIGHT AGAINST DEATH CONTINUES...

HEMATOMAS REMOVED. HOW'S OUR PATIENT, MAGGIE?

PULSE AND RESPIRATION THE SAME, BEN, WHICH ISN'T GOOD!

AT LEAST HE'S HOLDING HIS OWN...

IF HE WASN'T AS STRONG AS A BULL IT WOULD'VE BEEN LIGHTS-OUT A HALF-HOUR AGO! TED, PREPARE TO EVACUATE THE ACCUMULATED FLUID.

BRAIN CELLS PROBABLY DAMAGED...

THIS POOR DEVIL REALLY HIT THE JACKPOT, DIDN'T HE, BEN?

HOW'S IT GOING, DAVID? THEY JUST ALERTED ME ABOUT THIS EMERGENCY CASE, AND THE NEWSPAPER BOYS ARE YELLING FOR A BULLETIN.

OVER TWO HOURS ON THE TABLE, HAROLD. BEN CASEY'S NEVER DONE A BETTER JOB, BUT... WELL...YOU KNOW HOW THESE SUBDURALS ARE. TOUCH-AND-GO!

THE CLOCK CONTINUES ITS RELENTLESS TICKING. AFTER TWO HOURS AND TWENTY-TWO MINUTES HAVE PASSED...

CLOSURE COMPLETED, BEN!

WHEEL HIM INTO RECOVERY, PLEASE! HAVE OXYGEN AND PLASMA STANDING BY!

I'M FOR A STEAMING CUP OF COFFEE. I'LL CHECK BACK WITH THE PATIENT IN ABOUT 5 MINUTES, TED. KEEP YOUR EYE ON HIM TILL THEN, WILL YOU?

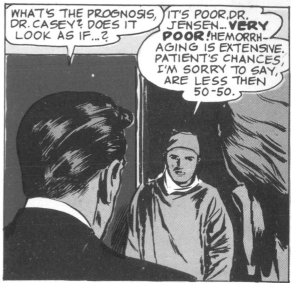

WHAT'S THE PROGNOSIS, DR. CASEY? DOES IT LOOK AS IF...?

IT'S POOR, DR. JENSEN... **VERY POOR!** HEMORRHAGING IS EXTENSIVE. PATIENT'S CHANCES, I'M SORRY TO SAY, ARE LESS THEN 50-50.

SORRY TO HEAR THAT, DR. CASEY, I'D APPRECIATE IT IF YOU WOULD PREPARE A BRIEF STATEMENT RIGHT AWAY. I'VE GOT AN OFFICE FULL OF REPORTERS HOWLING FOR NEWS. I LIKE TO KEEP THE PRESS SATISFIED.

THOSE REPORTERS... AND THE STATEMENT... WILL HAVE TO WAIT, DR. JENSEN. LET ME REMIND YOU THAT MY FIRST DUTY IS TO MY PATIENT, AND I INTEND TO GIVE HIM ALL THE HELP I CAN... AS LONG AS I CAN!

I'M QUITE AWARE OF YOUR RESPONSIBILITIES, DR. CASEY. AND IT MAY SURPRISE YOU TO KNOW THAT I'M CONSCIOUS OF MEDICAL ETHICS, AS WELL!

TEMPER, TEMPER! LET **ME** REMIND **YOU** THAT DR. JENSEN, AS MEDICAL SUPERINTENDENT, HAS **HIS** HEADACHES TOO! ONE OF THESE DAYS YOU'RE GOING TO CAUSE HIM AN APOPLECTIC FIT...

I... I CAN'T HELP IT. HE HAS A GENIUS FOR RUBBING ME THE WRONG WAY...

SIMMER DOWN, BEN CASEY. YOU JUST PERFORMED A BRILLIANT OPERATION, NOW IT'S TIME TO RELAX A BIT. DON'T FRET ABOUT REPORTERS... JENSEN'S A PAST MASTER AT STALLING THE PRESS.

SAY... WHY SHOULD REPORTERS BE INTERESTED IN **JACK GATLING**, ANYWAY?

THEY'RE NOT REALLY INTERESTED IN **HIM**, BEN... IT'S BECAUSE OF BRENT CALHOON'S CONNECTION WITH THE CASE THAT EVERYONE'S GOT THE HEEBY-JEEBIES.

BRENT CAL... **OF COURSE!** THEY PROBABLY WANT TO PIN A MEDAL ON THAT GALLANT GENTLEMAN.

UNLESS I'VE LOST MY NOSE FOR NEWS, THEY'RE MORE LIKELY TO DECORATE MR. CALHOON WITH A DONKEY'S TAIL! THIS TIME HE'S SURE TO BE CAST AS THE COWARDLY VILLAIN WHO DIDN'T FIGHT BY THE MARQUIS OF QUEENSBURY RULES!

DR. CASEY... **DR. BEN CASEY!** WANTED IN EMERGENCY RECOVERY! DR. CASEY....

THAT CALL, TED... WHAT...?

IT'S ALL OVER, BEN. THE POOR LITTLE GUY JUST... WELL... I'M TERRIBLY SORRY!

YOU DID EVERYTHING A DOCTOR **COULD**, BEN... AND MORE SKILLFULLY THEN ANY OTHER NEUROSURGEON I KNOW.

L-LET'S GET OUT OF HERE, THAT CUP OF COFFEE... I'D LIKE IT **NOW**!

TEN MINUTES LATER, BEN PAYS A VISIT TO THE SUITE OF BRENT CALHOON...

SEEMS I WAS RIGHT IN MY PRELIM DIAGNOSIS EARLIER THIS EVENING... SEVERE LACERATIONS AND TRANSVERSE FRACTURE OF THE UPPER JAW, WITH POSSIBLE INVOLVEMENT OF THE MAXILLARY SINUS. COULD BE WORSE... A **LOT** WORSE.

WANT... TO THANK YOU... HELP... TONIGHT. I WANT... YOU... TREAT ME.

WE HAVE AN EXCELLENT ORAL SURGEON HERE AT THE HOSPITAL, MR. CALHOON. NAME'S DR. CHANNING... HE'LL BE IN TO SEE YOU LATER TODAY. IN THE MEANTIME, I INSIST YOU KEEP YOUR JAW IMMOBLILIZED AS MUCH AS POSSIBLE. THAT MEANS **NO TALKING!**

BRENT AND I ARE SURE THIS DR. CHANNING IS A FIRST-RATE SPECIALIST, BUT BRENT... WELL... HE INSISTS ON **YOU**, DR. CASEY!

VERY FLATTERING. PERHAPS, THOUGH, I'D BETTER STRAIGHTEN YOU OUT ABOUT SOMETHING RIGHT NOW.

WE DON'T BREAK THE RULES FOR **ANYONE** HERE AT "59 WEST," NO MATTER HOW IMPORTANT THEY ARE. I'M THE RESIDENT NEUROSURGEON, AND THIS IS A CASE FOR AN ORAL SURGEON... AND IT WILL BE AN ORAL SURGEON WHO WILL HANDLE IT! HAVE I MADE MYSELF CLEAR?

Y-YES, DR. CASEY... PERFECTLY CLEAR.

IF THAT'S ALL, I'D BETTER GET ON TO MY OTHER PATIENTS. I'LL LOOK IN ON YOU FROM TIME TO TIME...

OH! ONE OTHER THING, DR. CASEY. ABOUT THAT MAN BRENT... ER... QUARRLED WITH? HOW... HOW IS **HE**

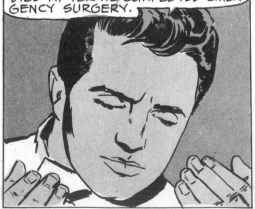

I MIGHT AS WELL TELL YOU RIGHT NOW, AND AVOID THE RISK OF HAVING YOU LEARN ABOUT IT IN A MORE PAINFUL WAY. JACK GATLING NEVER REGAINED CONSCIOUSNESS. HE... DIED AFTER WE COMPLETED EMERGENCY SURGERY.

OH, NO.. **NO! HOW TERRIBLE!**

THERE WAS ABSOLUTELY NOTHING WE COULD DO TO SAVE HIM. I'M SORRY... FOR **ALL** OF US. NOW, IF YOU'LL EXCUSE ME...

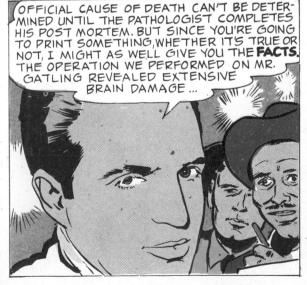

DON'T YOU THINK IT MIGHT BE WISER TO WAIT FOR THE AUTOPSY, MR. AGNEW.

WER'E NOT CHILDREN, DR. CASEY! A WHOLE ROOMFUL OF PEOPLE SAW BRENT CALHOON DELIVER A BLOW FROM WHICH DECEDENT NEVER RECOVERED. IF THE SUSPECT WASN'T SO...AH... **PROMINENT**...WE COULD REMAIN CALM AND LEVELHEADED. BUT WITH THE PUBLIC SHRIEKING FOR ACTION...

...YOU WANT A **SCALP** TO NAIL TO THE WALL. IN THIS CASE, THAT HAPPENS TO BELONG TO A WORLD FAMOUS CELEBRITY NAMED BRENT CALHOON, AM I RIGHT? BEFORE YOU DO **ANYTHING**, MR. AGNEW, I SUGGEST YOU LISTEN TO HOW ANY COMPETENT ATTORNEY COULD WRECK YOUR CASE.

START TALKING, CASEY!

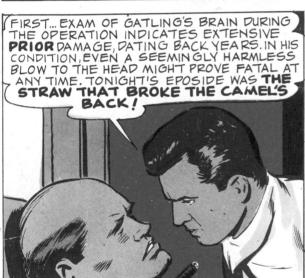

FIRST... EXAM OF GATLING'S BRAIN DURING THE OPERATION INDICATES EXTENSIVE **PRIOR** DAMAGE, DATING BACK YEARS. IN HIS CONDITION, EVEN A SEEMINGLY HARMLESS BLOW TO THE HEAD MIGHT PROVE FATAL AT ANY TIME. TONIGHT'S EPOSIDE WAS **THE STRAW THAT BROKE THE CAMEL'S BACK!**

VERY CATCHY PHRASE, CASEY...MIND IF I USE IT SOMETIME? YOUR PLEA WAS STIRRING, BUT IT DOESN'T ALTER THE FACT THAT IT WAS **CALHOON** WHO DELIVERED THE FINAL BLOW THAT PROVED FATAL. THAT'S AT LEAST **MANSLAUGHTER!**

LET ME CONTINUE TO MY **SECOND** POINT, MR. AGNEW.

I HAVE REASON TO BELIEVE THE DECEASED WAS A PROFESSIONAL BOXER, LISCENSED BY STATE AUTHORITIES TO FIGHT IN THE PRIZE RING. IF I'M RIGHT, THEN GATLING'S FISTS ARE CONCIDERED **LETHAL WEAPONS**, AREN'T THEY?

T-THE COURTS HAVE RULED SO IN THE PAST. WE CAN CHECK ON GATLING'S STATUS EASILY ENOUGH. IF HE **IS** LICENSED, HIS FINGERPRINTS WILL BE ON FILE. GO ON, DOCTOR...

IF GATLING...**KID GATT** IN THE RING, I UNDERSTAND... **WAS** A FIGHTER, THEN YOU HAVE NO CASE AGAINST BRENT CALHOON!

AREN'T YOU BEING A BIT HASTY IN DISMISSING THE CASE, DOCTOR. THERE ARE DOZENS OF WITNESSES...

...WHO SAW A LICENSED BOXER USE **LETHAL WEAPONS**...HIS **FISTS**...IN AN ATTACK ON ANOTHER INDIVIDUAL. THAT MAKES THE ATTACKER AS GUILTY OF A FELONY AS IF HE USED A KNIFE OR A GUN!

CALHOON'S ARGUMENT, THEN, WOULD BE THAT HE DEFENDED HIMSELF AGAINST CRIMINIAL ATTACK BY A FELON, EH? HUMM. YOU'RE RIGHT, MEDIC... **WE HAVE NO CASE AGAINST** THE ACTOR.! JUST TO TIE THINGS UP NEATLY... AND MARK THE FOLDER "CASE CLOSED"... I'LL VERIFY GATLING-GATT'S STATUS AS A BOXER, DR. JENSEN..?

PATHOLOGY HAS ALREADY STARTED ON THE AUTOPOSY. YOU'LL HAVE IT AS SOON AS POSSIBLE... JUST FOR YOUR RECORDS, OF COURSE.

THANKS FOR YOUR COOPERATION, DOCTORS. NEXT TIME I'M LOOKING FOR A CLEVER LAWYER, I'LL KNOW EXACTLY WHERE TO FIND HIM. NOW, IF YOU DON'T MIND...

JUST ONE OTHER MATTER, MR. AGNEW!

WE'VE CLEARED UP THE **LEGAL** ASPECTS OF THE CASE...THERE'S STILL A **MORAL** QUESTION OF CALHOON'S GUILT OR INNOCENCE. THE PRESS WILL DESTROY HIM UNLESS SOMEONE IN AUTHORITY EXPLAINS THAT GATLING WAS A MAN LIVING ON BORROWED TIME.

YOU'RE RIGHT, AS USUAL! LET THE REPORTERS IN...I'LL GIVE 'EM A STATEMENT!

AS MR. AGNEW SPEAKS, A HUSH FALLS ON THE ROOM. WHEN HE FINISHES...

DOES THIS GUY CALHOON KNOW HOW MUCH HE OWES YOU, CASEY?

QUITE A SIDELINE YOU GOT, DOC. IN ADDITION TO LIVES, YOU SAVE **REPUTATIONS**! MIND IF I KEEP THAT PICTURE WE GOT OF YOU IN THE CORRIDOR? I'D LIKE IT FOR MY SCRAPBOOK...**THE DAY FRESH REPORTER ALMOST GOT CLOBBERED BY PRETTY REMARKABLE MEDIC!**

DOCTOR!

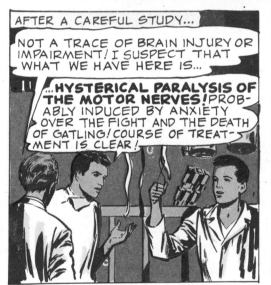

BUT THE NEXT DAY...

SURGERY... NOT PSYCHIATRY! CASEY... YOU **OPERATE** ON ME!

THE DAYS GO BY, AND BRENT CALHOON'S ANSWER REMAINS. THE SAME. FINALLY...

OPERATE! **SURGERY!**

TIME WE WENT INTO A HUDDLE, DR. ZORBA! I HAVE AN IDEA I'D LIKE TO DISCUSS... IN YOUR OFFICE, WHERE WE CAN HAVE COMPLETE PRIVACY.

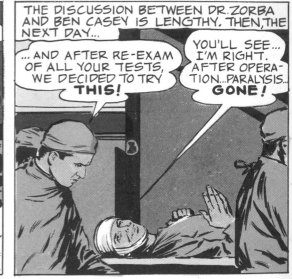

AGREED... SURGERY HAS BECOME AN OB- SESSION WITH CALHOON, AND HE THINKS OF IT AS A MEANS OF DOING PENANCE FOR GATLING'S DEATH. NOW, THIS IDEA YOU MENTIONED...

EVERY DAY HE REMAINS PARALYZED IS A DAY LOST! WHAT I HAVE IN MIND IS... WELL... A SORT OF COMPRO- MISE I WOULDN'T NORMALLY MAKE. HERE'S MY PLAN...

THE DISCUSSION BETWEEN DR. ZORBA AND BEN CASEY IS LENGTHY. THEN, THE NEXT DAY...

... AND AFTER RE-EXAM OF ALL YOUR TESTS, WE DECIDED TO TRY **THIS!**

YOU'LL SEE... I'M RIGHT. AFTER OPERA- TION...PARALYSIS. **GONE!**

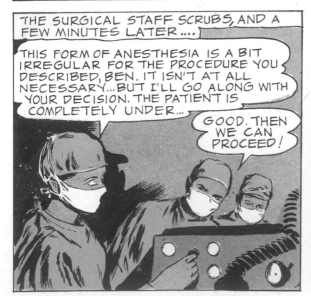

THE SURGICAL STAFF SCRUBS, AND A FEW MINUTES LATER....

THIS FORM OF ANESTHESIA IS A BIT IRREGULAR FOR THE PROCEDURE YOU DESCRIBED, BEN. IT ISN'T AT ALL NECESSARY...BUT I'LL GO ALONG WITH YOUR DECISION. THE PATIENT IS COMPLETELY UNDER...

GOOD. THEN WE CAN PROCEED!

START THE CLOCK! LET'S HOPE THIS WILL BE THE NEXT-TO-LAST CHAPTER OF THE CALHOON CAPER!

SUDDENLY...

WOULD YOU MIND TAKING OVER, DR. CHANNING? I'LL BE HAPPY TO ASSIST.

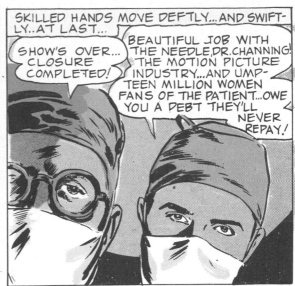

SKILLED HANDS MOVE DEFTLY...AND SWIFTLY..AT LAST...

SHOW'S OVER... CLOSURE COMPLETED!

BEAUTIFUL JOB WITH THE NEEDLE, DR. CHANNING! THE MOTION PICTURE INDUSTRY...AND UMP-TEEN MILLION WOMEN FANS OF THE PATIENT...OWE YOU A DEBT THEY'LL NEVER REPAY!

THANKS FOR THE DEMONSTRATION OF ORAL SURGERY, DR. CHANNING. I PLAN A REUNION OF THIS GALLANT CREW TOMORROW AFTER-NOON AT THREE, IN BRENT CALHOON'S SUITE. I'D LIKE YOU TO JOIN US.

THE FOLLOWING DAY, AT THE DESIG-NATED TIME AND PLACE...

...AND THIS IS DR. CARL CHANNING, WHO'S PART IN YESTERDAY'S SURGICAL EXTRAVAGANZA WAS TO TAKE CARE OF YOUR JAW, MR. CALHOON...MEET THE REST OF THE O.R. STAFF...I'VE GATHERED THEM HERE TO WATCH ONE OF YOUR MOST IN-SPIRING TRIUMPHS!

SURGERY YESTERDAY WAS A COMPLETE SUCCESS. YOUR JAW IS MENDING...AND I DEFY ANYONE TO FIND A TRACE OF PRESSURE ON THE BRAIN. NOW, MR. CALHOON...I WANT YOU TO **WALK!**

I... I'LL... TRY!

TED... NURSE WILLS... LEAVE THE PATIENT ALONE NOW! THAT WAS YOUR CUE, MR. CALHOON...WALK ACROSS-STAGE!

I... I **CAN** WALK! PARALYSIS... **GONE**...AS I...PREDICATED! **I CAN WALK AGAIN!**

THIS MAY WELL BE ONE OF YOUR MOST SUCCESSFUL PERFORMANCES, MR. CALHOON! **CONGRATULATIONS!**

THE CONGRATULATIONS...RIGHTFULLY **YOURS**... DR. CASEY! EXCELLENT... JOB OF SURGERY! ONE OTHER THING...

I COMMEND YOU... FOR GOOD SENSE... IN RESPECTING MY OPINION....THAT SURGERY... NECESSARY...IF I WAS TO WALK AGAIN! AFTER ALL... I HAVE VALUABLE...MEDICAL BACKGROUND MYSELF...FROM PLAYING PART... OF DR. FRANZ COBALT... IN "FROM... THESE BROKEN BONES"!

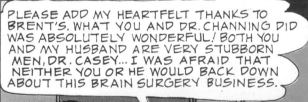

AFTER THE PARTY BREAKS UP...

PLEASE ADD MY HEARTFELT THANKS TO BRENT'S. WHAT YOU AND DR. CHANNING DID WAS ABSOLUTELY WONDERFUL! BOTH YOU AND MY HUSBAND ARE VERY STUBBORN MEN, DR. CASEY... I WAS AFRAID THAT NEITHER YOU OR HE WOULD BACK DOWN ABOUT THIS BRAIN SURGERY BUSINESS.

WHICH REMINDS ME... IS THERE ANY SPECIAL POST-OPERATIVE TREATMENT NECESSARY BECAUSE OF THE BRAIN SURGERY?

I HAVE A CONFESSION TO MAKE, MRS. CALHOON... IT MUSTN'T GET BACK TO YOUR HUSBAND. NOT YET, ANYWAY!

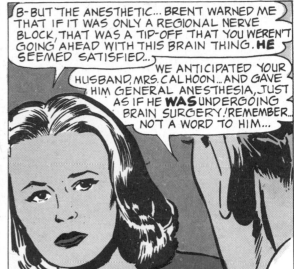

THE DOG THAT 'TALKED'

Wesley Crispin let the flame from his lighter reach out and lick the end of the cigarette which dangled from his lips. The tissue-thin paper curled away from the flame and yellowish flakes of tobacco glowed white-hot. Inhaling deeply, he felt the heat searing down his throat. Through the swirl of smoke expelled from his nostrils, he glanced nervously around the garage. He needed this cigarette desperately . . . a stark tragedy like the one which had just occurred here could really break a man up if he didn't steady himself at once. Marion was dead!

Wesley Crispin watched with half-averted eyes as the police checked the exhaust pipe of the car, examined the window of the cement-block garage, tested the door that led to the kitchen of his house. Through the pounding that had started in his temples he was aware of whispering voices on all sides—questions asked tersely, responses muttered in grim monosyllables. These men who had come in answer to his phone call were veterans at this sort of thing he realized, observing with unconscious admiration the precision with which they went about their grisly task. They were well-acquainted with disaster and knew exactly how to behave in the presence of tragedy. But, with all their experience and skill, there was nothing any of them could do. Marion was dead!

Wesley Crispin saw the white-coated attendants moving past him, silently trudging by with the shapeless bundle which had been his wife until a short while ago. The garage door sighed back on its rollers, and they were gone. So was a part of his life . . . ten years of it, if you counted the time they were engaged before he and Marion had been married. A full decade of squabbling and loving and planning and disappointments. It was all over now. Kaput. Finito. Marion was dead!

"Wesley Crispin, isn't it?" The chunky man in the shiny blue-serge suit inquired, consulting a grubby notebook, and he turned to face this stranger who had been introduced as Dr. Something-or-other, the Coroner.

"Mr. Crispin," the man repeated softly, "I'd like to hear once again, if you don't mind, the exact circumstances under which you found your wife here in the garage. There are several areas I'd like clarified . . ."

Wesley Crispin felt a trifle queasy and his head had begun to ache in earnest—but he forced himself to concentrate on the answers which Blue-Serge seemed to need. Only vaguely aware of his own words, he told the chunky man the same story he had given to the police as soon as they arrived: the car motor running in the closed garage when he reached home; the startled discovery of his wife slumped over the steering wheel; his wild scurrying to open doors; the frantic attempt to revive her. All pointless, of course. By the time he reached her, Marion was dead.

"And the dog?" the chunky man asked, almost in a whisper.

"Old 'Turk' was still breathing," Wesley Crispin answered, concentrating on the clumsy knot of the Coroner's faded red tie. "It was really more like gagging, but I got him outside fast . . . and he seemed all right by the time the police got here. Staggered a bit, at first, but the neighbors took him and I guess he's okay now."

Wesley Crispin heard what must have been a signal of departure and, as the police filed past him, each man bowed his head slightly and grumbled words meant to be consoling. Each of them were obviously embarrassed and uncomfortable and anxious to express his sympathy. All but the chunky Coroner. Snapping his notebook shut, the man in the blue-serge suit sighed heavily, and trudged away without a word.

* * * * *

Wesley Crispin stared at his hands and realized, for the first time, how gruff the chunky man's voice was.

"Quite frankly," the Coroner was saying, "I had grave reservations about your story, Mr. Crispin. The pathology report was quite revealing. It showed that your late wife had particles of brown wool in her throat and nose. Evidence, I felt, that she had been suffocated by the blanket we found in the rear seat of the car. By starting the motor and letting it run for awhile in the tightly-shut garage, you merely made it look like an accident or suicide. A simple check of your late wife's blood proved what I suspected . . . the carbon monoxide content was normal. The poor woman, therefore, was murdered before you started the motor."

"Who tipped you off? Or what?" Someone asked.

"The dog," the chunky Coroner said. "If enough carbon monoxide had escaped into the garage to kill the victim, as we were supposed to believe—it would certainly have done the same to an ancient pooch like old 'Turk'."

Wesley Crispin stared at the dull grey handcuffs encircling his wrists. Marion was dead . . . so was his plan to get away with the murder of the nagging women he had begun to hate almost ten years before.

Wesley Crispin could think of only one thing: he needed a cigarette desperately. A tragedy like the one which had just occurred could really break a man up if he didn't steady himself at once.

DEAD ON TIME

D R. BEN CASEY stepped out of the city's main bookstore armed with a weighty volume on medical history and a smaller one dealing with the work of Sir Frederick Grant Banting, the Canadian doctor who succeeded in isolating insulin.

It was Dr. Casey's intention to spend the remainder of this pleasant summer evening on some intensive, and enjoyable, reading.

Outside the store the sidewalk was busy with hurrying crowds. Lightly humming a tune to himself, Ben was crossing to his parked car when three men burst out of the side entrance of the City and Merchants' Bank.

The first two were carrying bulging sacks. The third was brandishing a Navy Colt gun. All were wearing nylon stocking masks.

The man with the gun snarled: "Outa the way, folks, unless anybody wants a bullet!"

Ben dived behind his car and swung the

heaviest of his recent purchases with all the power at his command.

Zunk!

The big book slammed the gun from the bandit's grasp.

Instantly, the two other men fired wildly from the big saloon car they had just leaped into. The bullets went astray, and in the next instant there was another blast.

It came from a revolver fired by a hurrying police officer—and the third man let out a yelp and reeled crazily over the sidewalk.

Two other policemen raced towards the spot, but before they could reach it the wounded bandit was forcibly dragged into the saloon which made off at high speed down the city street.

One of the policemen knelt and fired at the retreating car.

Zing ... Wheeee ... Bam!

The slugs hit the rear fender, but the car sped on—and in another moment was lost to sight in the traffic.

The officer came upright just as Ben neared him.

"You catch a glimpse of their faces, buster?" asked the officer.

Ben shook his head.

"I guess nobody did," he said. "They were wearing stocking masks."

"Yeah, saw one of them like that—I just wondered about the others. Thanks, anyway. . . ." He broke off as a prowl car roared up, its siren screaming.

Ben watched the car give chase, but privately reflected that the bank raiders had got a start which would make it difficult to catch up with them.

He joined several other passers-by in making statements, then climbed into his own car and headed for 59 West.

But his intention of putting in some quiet reading seemed to have receded—the events of the last half-hour had made Ben feel restless.

He went in for a chat with Dr. David Zorba. The latter listened to his account of the incident, then said slowly: "The bandit who was shot, Ben—d'you know if he was gravely injured?"

"I guess not, Doctor. I mean I don't know, not for sure. It was kind of difficult to decide

exactly where the bullet penetrated—and before anybody could intervene he had been dragged into the getaway car."

"H'm." Zorba fingered his lean chin. "If the fellow is badly hurt he could be in a serious plight without medical attention."

"That's true, but I reckon there isn't anything to be done about it," rejoined Ben. "They certainly won't be in any hurry to take their pal to hospital—that's for sure!"

"There's too much violence these days, Ben. . . ."

"That's only too sadly true, Doctor." A thought struck Ben and he went on: "If the shot bandit *is* hurt bad that may help the police."

"Meaning?"

"They may have to get some kind of medical aid. Like contacting a druggist if they daren't risk trying to get a doctor."

"H'm," said Zorba again. "I don't care to say it, Ben, but there are some doctors who have been known to betray their calling by rendering assistance to wounded gangsters. . . ."

Ben eyed him for a moment. "It's a fine point whether such a doctor *is* betraying his code, isn't it?" he asked. "I mean it is the bounden duty of a medic to give aid to the suffering. I don't know that there is anything in the code about the character of the suffering person!"

Zorba smiled. "Well, yes, that's true enough. We *do* have this duty to alleviate pain.

However, what I was considering was the kind of crooked doctor—they're happily very rare, of course—who deliberately makes his services available to gangsters in return for money."

"You mean one who acts for a gang regularly, like he's on their payroll?"

Zorba nodded. "Yes," he said. "If there is no crooked medic in this town then the plight of this bandit could well become serious—the danger of gangrene in an untended wound can be very real, as you know."

"Well," said Ben, "I still don't know what we can do about it, but you may be right in thinking the set-up could help the police in their search."

Just then the telephone clamoured. Ben picked up the receiver.

"Police Headquarters speaking," a voice said. "We're asking all hospitals and doctors to report any requests for emergency treatment."

"Who's speaking—personally, I mean?"

"This is Captain Granger. . . ."

"I figured I knew your voice, captain. This is Dr. Casey. We have met."

"Oh, hello then—I gather you were an eyewitness of the incident, Doc?"

"Yeah."

"We thought the hoods might try to persuade a doctor to attend an emergency case outside of his hospital or private surgery. If any call of that kind comes to you please contact us without delay."

"Will do, captain."

"The officer who fired thinks the bandit may have been shot in the body, not just a hand or arm. In that case the chances are the guy'll be needing surgery pretty desperately."

"Could be, captain. What we call a red blanket case."

"Yeah—well, if anything remotely suspicious comes up ring us at once."

Ben hung up and reported the gist of the conversation to Dr. Zorba. After a little while, he left to go to his room. He was going down a long, cool corridor when the night sister came hurrying towards him.

Ben was giving a smiling greeting when he noticed the worried look on her face.

"Anything wrong, sister?" he asked.

"Oh, Dr. Casey, I'm sure I don't know—but Anne has disappeared."

"Disappeared?" echoed Ben.

"She was already overdue and I went to make inquiries . . . she hasn't been seen in the last hour!"

Anne Kirk was a student nurse and Ben knew she was wholly dedicated to her calling. It seemed odd that she should fail to check in for duty.

"She went out this afternoon to do some shopping—in her uniform, as a matter of fact. She just hasn't returned. . . ."

"Maybe she ran into a friend and got delayed talking," Ben began—but even as he spoke the words their improbability struck him. He knew and liked Anne and it was utterly foreign to her nature to be late.

"We'd better report to Dr. Zorba," he said. "I'll come along with you."

As they went into the office they saw Dr. Zorba holding the telephone receiver. There was a strange, tense look on his face.

Then they heard a click. Zorba let the receiver slide back on its rest and turned to them.

"It's happened, Ben," he said.

"What . . . what's happened?" asked Ben quickly.

"The gangsters—one of them was on the phone." Zorba passed a hand across his forehead. "Only it wasn't the way either we or the police figured . . . Ben, those hoods have kidnapped one of our student nurses!"

"Anne Kirk?"

Zorba nodded. "Oh, I see sister must have informed you of her absence. Yes, they picked her up off the sidewalk on account of she was wearing her uniform. They're holding her prisoner to attend to the shot gangster—only now they say they must have a doctor. The man was shot in the stomach and he's in mighty bad shape."

There was a silence.

"And if we phone the law?" asked Ben, though he sensed only too grimly what the answer would be.

"We'll never see Anne Kirk again if we call Police Headquarters—that was the message."

"And?"

"They want a doctor to be at the intersection of Twenty-second and Alison streets fifteen minutes from now," said Zorba dully. "He will be picked up by car and taken to the gang's hideout. If the wounded man is given proper treatment they promise that both the doctor and nurse Kirk will be released within a week."

Ben bit down on his lip.

"One of us has got to go," he said at length.

"Yes." Zorba spoke slowly. He eyed Ben levelly, then said: "It's a risk, isn't it?"

Ben nodded. It was much more than a risk, he knew. The chances were that neither the doctor nor Anne Kirk would ever be seen alive again! Only too well did he understand the ruthlessness of hoodlums in such desperate circumstances.

"They're not likely to turn either the doctor or Anne Kirk loose to testify against them on a witness stand," said Zorba. "I just can't ask any doctor under my control to do it!" He reached for his hat.

"Where are you going, Doctor?" asked Ben quietly.

"I just told you I can't ask anyone else, Ben. . . . I'm going to do it myself!"

"Doctor—you can't do it, it's suicide. The hospital needs you. Look, I'll. . . ."

Zorba smiled faintly, "It's like you, Ben— I know you're willing to take the risk yourself, but I'm not going to let you do it."

"You can't stop me. . . ."

"I'm still in charge, Ben," responded Zorba quietly. "I . . ." He stopped, looking hard at his colleague. "Have you thought of something?"

"Yeah . . . it might just work. We've got to try it, anyway!"

"If you've got a plan you'd better tell me. . . ."

"It depends on one factor," answered Ben. "One of the porters here has a powerful motorcycle . . . I only hope he isn't out on it right now!"

"He just rode in on it ten minutes ago. But

why? What on earth has Jed's noisy motor-cycle got to do with this situation?"

"Everything," replied Ben with a grin.

*   *   *

Exactly fifteen minutes later Dr. David Zorba, carrying his emergency bag, was standing at the intersection. He didn't have to wait.

A black Lincoln town car cruised against the kerb and a harsh voice said: "You the doc?"

Dr. Zorba nodded.

"Inside, fellow—you're wanted and bad!"

The door was held open and Zorba stepped inside. Instantly, another man rammed a gun against his side.

"No tricks, Doc!" he snarled.

"I've come on an errand of medical mercy, my friend," said Dr. Zorba impassively. He

waved a hand. "You can see for yourself that there is no one else around."

"Okay, let's go." The gunner stared around. "Nah, there's no car following and no coppers lurking—only some punk kid on a motor-cycle away in the distance. All right, Al—give her the gas!"

The big car roared though the gears and in another seven minutes they were hitting ninety on Route Seventy-six.

Dr. Zorba stared into the reflecting mirror. There was no sign of the "punk kid" on his motor-cycle—but the doctor knew he was hard on the trail, just far enough behind to be unseen.

The ride took all of thirty minutes. Now they were out in open country, diving down side roads until, finally, they came to a white-painted bungalow surrounded by a trimly-kept lawn.

Dr. Zorba's eyebrows lifted fractionally. The gang, he reflected, evidently did themselves well.

"Okay, this is it—out and no funny business," Al snapped.

Dr. Zorba stepped out—and, with the gun jammed into his back, ascended three wide steps and went into the bungalow.

"We had a guy watching Police Headquarters just in case any prowl car zoomed out this-away," said Al with an evil grin on his tight face. "Okay—I guess you just had sense enough not to call the coppers. Inside this room—on your left."

Zorba walked in—to see a man lying groaning on a bed. By the side of it stood Anne Kirk, her pretty face pale and drawn but her eyes courageous.

Dr. Zorba placed a kindly hand on her shoulder, then examined the wounded man.

"Well?" rapped Al.

"This man needs surgery," said Zorba.

"Okay—then get on with it."

"He needs hospitalization," said Dr. Zorba gently.

"Don't give us that," the other said. "He ain't gonna be taken to no hospital. You can do what's necessary right here—and don't waste any more time."

"Very well." Zorba issued crisp instructions to Anne and prepared to administer an anaesthetic.

"How long will it take?" Al said.

"That will depend on the precise location of the bullet and any other intervening factors. . . ."

"We don't want no medical lecture, Doc—get moving, will ya?"

Zorba shrugged. He took the fitted-up hypodermic from Anne and gave the injection.

Then, slowly and carefully, he laid out his instruments while Anne brought more boiling water.

"Is he hurt real bad?" asked one of the other hoods.

"Pretty bad—if you hadn't called medical aid he'd have died."

"I guess I don't want to see you slice him," the hood muttered. He shambled towards the door.

"You're yellow, Joe, that's what," jeered Al.

Zorba glanced at Anne.

"You're a student nurse, my dear," he said gently. "I don't think you've yet watched an operation, have you?"

Dumbly, she shook her head.

"I'm afraid you're going to have to watch this one," said Dr. Zorba. "I'm sorry it's not in rather different circumstances. . . ."

Anne smiled bravely. "I'll be all right, Dr. Zorba," she said. "I won't let you down."

"I knew that already, Anne. All right, now we begin. . . ."

Ben had ridden the motor-cycle hugging the side of the road and always keeping far back. Often he had to deliberately lose sight of his quarry—for if the gangsters once understood that they were being followed the plan would have been placed in peril.

Fortunately, the roadway had a number of acute bends so that he was able to follow without much risk of discovery.

The advantage was increased when the black car plunged down narrow, winding side roads. It was when he went down an incline that, staring ahead, Ben could just see the car—almost a speck in the distance—turning abruptly into an even narrower road, one that was little more than a cindered pathway.

It was almost dark now. Ben cut his lights and rode slowly ahead. Then he dismounted and went on foot until he was at the bungalow.

The black car was parked in the driveway and lights shone from the house itself.

Ben paused. His medical experience told him that surgery must inevitably take some time. It would be madness for him to intervene now.

He almost crawled to the side of the house. A brief search enabled him to find what he sought—telephone wires. He got a jack-knife out and cut the flex cable!

Then he went back to his machine and rode half a mile down the road to where he recalled having passed a pay telephone booth.

Two minutes later he stepped out—with the knowledge that Captain Lou Granger and two prowl cars were even now zooming through the night. And that nobody could phone that news to the bungalow.

He swung himself astride the big twin-cylinder motor-cycle and was soon back at the bungalow.

This time he stood in the porch. But no sound of movement came to him. Gently, he pushed at the door. It opened noiselessly inwards.

Ben was tiptoeing across the hall when he heard a small sound from a room. He flattened himself against the wall just in the nick of time.

A man smoking a raddled cigarette came through the door and turned—to stare him full in the face!

Ben brought his left fist up in a shattering haymaker. The blow took the gangster on the point of the jaw, almost lifting him clear of the flooring. For a second he rocked back, then pitched forward headlong into Ben's arms.

By a mighty effort, Ben steadied himself so that they both went down without more than the merest sound. Then he dragged the knocked-out man back into the room and left him bound and gagged in a wall closet.

Breathing heavily, Ben went back into the hall and across to the opposite door. Sounds came to him—the small movements of people and the subdued buzz of desultory talk.

He placed his ear against the jamb of the door.

"You through, Doc?" a voice grated.

"In one more minute, I think," said a voice Ben recognized as Dr. Zorba's, though the words were spoken in no more than a whisper.

"And Eddie'll be okay?"

"Yes, but he'll need rest—and he'll also need to have his wound dressed."

"Oh . . . you mean somebody'll have to stay with him." Al shrugged. "The nurse she can stick around, I guess."

"I see."

"You, too, Doc . . . you ain't going to leave here yet. Eddie might need you."

"When . . ." began Dr. Zorba.

"You'll both be free to go when we say," said Al. There was an odd note in his voice and Ben compressed his lips. He knew—as Dr. Zorba did—that the gang had no intention of letting their prisoners go free.

Al lit a cigarette and went on suddenly: "Say, Sam—there should've been a phone call from Zack by now."

"Maybe he got delayed. . . ."

"I don't pay guys to get themselves delayed. I guess I'll call that place he sometimes stops off at and. . . ." There was the sound of a phone being dialled.

Ben waited, scarcely breathing.

Then Al was speaking again—in a tight, deadly voice.

"Sump'n queer going on . . . *the line's dead!*"

"What?"

"Yeah, I don't get it." Al started for the door. Ben moved back down the hall and hid behind a jutting section of the wall. In a few seconds Al was back.

"The wire's been cut!" he yelped. "Somebody's on to us. Hey—where's Joe?"

Ben waited another moment. The door burst open and the two gangsters raced for the opposite room. Ben slid into the first room and locked the door.

"Through the window—both of you," he said urgently to Dr. Zorba and Anne.

Wild yells greeted them from outside, then there was a tremendous hammering on the door.

"Round to the window—don't let them escape!" bellowed Al. "It's a trick, but we're dead on time . . . and so will they be if they try to make a getaway and . . . *whassat?*"

There was a roar of engines and a shrill wailing from police sirens.

"It's the coppers—we're done for!" screamed Al.

The gangsters raced for the rear exit—only to walk straight into the arms of six hard-eyed patrolmen armed with guns!

In another minute the gangsters were wearing steel bracelets. Al looked up pallidly as he saw Ben.

"You're the guy who threw that book at Eddie!" he screeched. "Doggone it—it was you put the cops on to us . . . but . . . but how?"

"I cut your phone cable and went back down the road to a pay booth," said Ben. "When you take to a life of crime you should think of every trick."

Captain Granger went into the lounge and stared down at the unconscious man.

"He gonna be okay, Doc?"

Dr. Zorba nodded. "Oh, yes, he'll get well . . . though I guess I got here just in time."

"Otherwise it'd have been a case of dead on time, eh?"

"Well," murmured Dr. Zorba, "you know, captain, I think it was our Dr. Casey who really got here dead on time. . . ."

Trouble Times Two!

THE telephone jangled at his elbow. Lester Dingwall put aside the magazine he'd been reading, reached for the instrument and, cradling it between shoulder and ear, mumbled and grumphed into it several times. Yawning, he replaced the receiver and got to his feet.

"Emergency at 232 Kemp Street," he announced to Jeff, who was already slipping into his white duty jacket. "Mrs. Alonzo Kendrick tells me she's having trouble with little Bernard. We'd better slip anchor and help rescue Little B."

Racing across town, with the siren clearing traffic from the path of the ambulance, Lester confided to Jeff that he was seriously considering the purchase of a pet. What he needed was companionship and the magazine he'd been studying offered some nice puppies and kittens...

"Don't do it," Jeff said flatly, his eyes darting about the road in search of hidden enemies as he steered the heavy vehicle. "I had a dog once, myself. And a cat, two goldfish, a canary and three turtles. **Don't do it!** A dog is for the birds..."

"Hmmm," reflected Lester Dingwall, toying with an idea. "I think you've got something there. A **bird**-dog might be just what I need."

In answer, Jeff swung the wheel tight and jammed on the brakes. "232 Kemp," he announced. "That's probably your customer pacing up and down in front of the yaller house right now."

Lester grabbed his bag and hastened to the side of Mrs. Kendrick, who heaved a sigh of relief when she saw him, then immediately began to berate him for taking so long while little Bernard was trapped down there in the basement experiencing excruciating pain because he had gotten inextricably caught in the washing machine and being only a three-year-old baby couldn't be expected to get himself out or understand that help was on the way...

"Let's have a look at Little Bernard," Lester said, shifting his chewing gum from the left cheek to his right as he followed Mrs. Kendrick into the house. Even before she flung open the door of the little laundry room Lester could hear the kid's wailing. Sure enough, the little tyke **was** stuck inside the washer.

"All right little man,' 'he cooed as he approached the machine. "Uncle Lester'll have you out and good as new in a jiff."

There was violent movement inside the washer and a baby face peered up at Lester. He gulped involuntarily and almost swallowed his chewing gum. Little Bernard was quite obviously a **monkey!**

Seven minutes later, after being scratched, screamed and spit at all through the operation, Lester managed to disengage the animal from the agitator which had held its tail and, consequently, made a prisoner of Little Bernard.

Mrs. Kendrick gathered the quivering animal into her arms and, scolding it for being a naughty boy, assured it that she wouldn't let bad mans hurt-um anymore. Lester started toward the stairs, reprimanding Mrs. Kendrick for calling an ambulance on such a mission. Suddenly, a tin can thudded against his back and Lester whirled in time to see Little Bernard preparing to pelt him again. With a snort, Lester dodged through a curtain of flying objects and, trapping the animal, carried it over to a spot where the light was better. Putting the screeching monkey across his knee, he began to administer a lusty spanking.

At that moment he heard a cry of dismay and, looking up, realized that Mrs. Kendrick was approaching him with homicide in her eyes. Only two steps away, one of her feet shot out from under her and, skidding on a tin can that Little Bernard had thrown, Mrs. Kendrick sprawled full-length on the floor. A quick glance was all that Lester needed: Mrs. Kendrick has just suffered a Greenstick Fracture of the Left Tibia.

Working with speed born of long experience...and despite the determined efforts of screaming, clawing Little Bernard to keep him from successfully accomplishing his task...Lester managed to splint Mrs. Kendrick's ankle. No sooner had he finished than he heard a step on the stairs and, looking up, saw a scowling, heavy-set man descending ponderously toward him. A momentary flicker of apprehension vanished as soon as Lester learned the gentleman was Mr. Kendrick.

Together they carried the moaning woman upstairs and, having stowed her away in bed, Lester turned to go. A quick handshake, a mumble that sounded like 'thnks fr yr hp," and Lester moved toward the front door. Before he could reach it, however, Lester felt a number of distinct raps and thwunks across his back, neck and shoulders. Ducking, he opened the door and darted through it, fleeing from the fusilade of objects with which Little Bernard was pelting him. Sprinting across the lawn, he caught a final glimpse of the monkey preparing to launch a heavy cut-glass vase filled with chrysanthemums.

In the safety of the ambulance, while Lester wiped the blood from several lacerations received within the hour, Jeff babbled excitedly about something he'd just found in the newspaper he'd been reading during this routine call.

"**Routine** call...?" Lester managed to splutter, turning baleful eyes on his partner.

"I been thinking over what you said before," Jeff blurted, pointing to the paper. "Here's a great idea... just what you been looking for. It's a real gasser of a pet, advertised FREE by a Mr. A. Kendrick...with a six-month supply of food thrown in! You'll never guess what this twerp wants to give away! It's a genuine..."

"Get this crate moving," Lester said in a low, dangerous voice that made Jeff pause and look at him in wonder. "I've decided not to have a pet after all," Lester said with curious finality. "I'm going to take up animal taxidermy as a hobby, instead."

DIAL EMERGENCY...

DANGLING AT THE END OF A TAUT ROPE, DR. DAN DAZZLER GROPED IN THE SEMI-DARKNESS OF THE DEEP EXCAVATION. DOWN THERE BELOW HIM— HYSTERICAL WITH PAIN AND FEAR— WAS A BOY WHOSE LIFE DEPENDED UPON THE YOUNG INTERNE'S SKILL AND COURAGE....

ON THE RARE OCCASIONS WHEN "EMERGENCY" IS SLOW, DR. DAN DAZZLER IS NEVER PUZZLED ABOUT HOW TO FILL IN HIS MOMENTS OF RELAXATION....

I'VE GOT THIS CROSSWORD BEATEN TO A FRAZZLE, SID... EXCEPT FOR ONE LAST ITEM. YOU KNOW A 7-LETTER WORD FOR "STUPID"?

"STUPID", EH? HOW ABOUT "JAY-WALKER", DOC? NAW... THAT'S 1-2-3... UH... 9 LETTERS.

SUDDENLY

EMERGENCY! VICINITY OF GREEN STREET AND JEFFERSON AVENUE. BOY... AGED 11... FALLEN INTO DEEP BUILDING EXCAVATION. EXTENT OF INJURIES UNKNOWN. PROCEED IMMEDIATELY!

LET'S GO, CHARIOT DRIVER!!

IN A MATTER OF SECONDS THE AMBULANCE ROARS OUT INTO CITY STREETS....

"STUPID", EH... IN 7 LETTERS? HOW ABOUT **TRAFFIC**?

RRROOOWWRR

IT'S BEEN EXCRU-CIATING FUN, SID. HERE'S WHERE THE CLEAN-CUT YOUNG MEDIC HITS THE SILK.... **GERONIMO!**

REEEEEE

YOU GOTTA **DO** SOMETHING, **DO** SOMETHING, OFFICER. MY MELVIN'S BEEN DOWN IN THAT HOLE FOR MORE THAN AN HOUR. WHATTA WE PAY OUR TAXES FOR, ANYWAY?

WE'RE DOING EVERYTHING WE CAN, MR. BLAIR. WE'LL HAVE YOUR SON OUT IN JUST A FEW MORE MINUTES.

YOU CAN SEE IT'S NARROW, DOC... AND **DEEP**....

...THE KID'S WEDGED IN MIGHTY TIGHT. I THINK MAYBE HIS ARM IS BUSTED. HE'S BEEN CRYING A LOT... LIKE HE'S IN PAIN.

A RESCUE ROPE IS ATTACHED TO DAN'S ANKLES AND, IN A FEW MOMENTS....

EASY DOES IT, BOYS. LET THE DOC SET THE PACE... LIKE HE'S CRAWLING DOWN WITH HIS HANDS.

C-CAN YOU HELP ME, MISTER? MY... MY ARM...PLEASE...

HAVE YOU OUT OF HERE IN A COUPLE OF MINUTES, MELVIN. JUST HOLD ON...

SID! SEND DOWN A SEDATIVE.

FRACTURE... BOTH THE RADIUS AND THE ULNA. ARM'S DEFORMED— THAT'S WHAT'S WEDGING KID IN AGAINST SIDE OF HOLE. BETTER GIVE HIM A SHOT TO EASE THE PAIN, THEN...

JUST RELAX, MELVIN ...I'M GOING TO MOVE YOUR ARM A BIT. **THERE**...**IT'S FREE**...!!

DROP ANOTHER LINE DOWN. MELVIN'S READY TO SURFACE!

GOOD WORK, DOC. KID'LL BE UP IN ANOTHER SECOND. IS IT SERIOUS?

FRACTURE... I CAN HAVE IT SET IN A JIFFY. LET'S HOPE THAT **SHOCK** ISN'T TOO BAD!

THERE! ALMOST AS GOOD AS NEW...

YOU... IN THE WHITE COAT. YOU'RE PRETTY YOUNG, AREN'T YOU? I'LL BET YOUR NOT **OLD ENOUGH** TO BE A DOCTOR.

WHEN I GET YOU TO THE HOSPITAL, MEL, I'LL DO A **REAL** PATCH JOB.

HOLD EVERYTHING, MISTER!

"CURES" ARE ALL AROUND US!

At one time or another almost every substance known to man has been used in the treatment of disease. Until relatively recent times any substance that was novel, hard-to-get and could be forced into the human body had its heyday as a "miracle drug." While a scant few actually had curative value, the vast majority were either harmful or totally useless. The old apothecary shop swarmed with such bizarre "cure-alls" as viper's flesh, crushed sow bugs and body lice, incinerated toads and powdered mummy!

Even after the Pharmacopeia was drastically revised in the 17th century—and many worthless items dropped—the sole of an old shoe "worn by some man that walked much" was retained as a splendid treatment for dysentery, when ground up and taken internally!

As late as the nineteenth century "Usnea" —moss scraped from the skull of a criminal who had been hung in chains—was believed to possess curative powers!

To this very day quacks and charlatans annually collect untold millions of dollars for worthless or even harmful "secret" remedies which succeed only in separating the desperate or gullible from their money!